指圧道
SHIATSU-DOH

指圧道

SHIATSU-DOH

Improved Health and Enhanced Living
Through the Japanese Healing Art

Kensen Saito

POUND PUBLISHING

First published 2003

Printed and bound in Canada on acid-free paper

Published by Pound Publishing
Pound Publishing Corporation, 17 Mount Royal Avenue, Toronto, Ontario, Canada M6H 2S2

Edited by Julia Armstrong

Designed by Rodrigo Bascuñán and Roberto Cortez, Pound Publishing

Canadian Cataloguing in Publication Data
Saito, Kensen, 1951-
        Shiatsu-Doh

This publication can be purchased in the United Kingdom and Japan from:

CROSS MEDIA LTD.
66 Wells Street, London WIT 3PY U.K.
Tel: +44 (0) 20-7436-1960
Fax: +44 (0) 20-7436-1930
E-mail: books@crossmedia.co.uk

ISBN 0-9733221-0-1

DEDICATED TO:

Tokujiro Sensei, Toru Sensei
and
My Mother

CONTENTS

FOREWORD   3
ACKNOWLEDGEMENTS   5
INTRODUCTION   6

CHAPTER 1
THE THUMB-PRESSURE HEALING ART AND ITS ORIGINS   8

CHAPTER 2
SHIATSU AT EVERY STAGE OF LIFE   28

CHAPTER 3
FROM TOKYO TO TORONTO: MY STORY   38

CHAPTER 4
EXECUTIVES, ATHLETES AND MOVIE STARS   50

CHAPTER 5
THE GREAT MENTOR IN MY LIFE   62

CHAPTER 6
THE BENEFITS OF SHIATSU: PATIENT TESTIMONIALS   78

CHAPTER 7
SHIATSU HELPS ATHLETES EXCEL   98

CHAPTER 8
SHIATSU: A FRIEND TO ENTERTAINERS   116

CHAPTER 9
WHAT YOU LEARN AS A SHIATSU PRACTITIONER   130

CHAPTER 10
THE INTERNATIONAL SCENE   144

RESOURCES AND CONTACTS   158

FOREWORD

"If you choose the right path, it will open up the world to you" was my elementary school song, and I still remember it 40 years later. Born and raised in Japan, I immigrated to Canada in 1979 and started practising shiatsu in Toronto. Eventually, I began to spread knowledge of shiatsu to all parts of the world. As I reflect on this, I realize just how far the path I chose has taken me in my life.

Shiatsu-doh means "the way of shiatsu," and for me this therapeutic art truly is a way of life – a path to physical and spiritual healing and, therefore, enhanced living. Thirty-five years have passed since I first had a therapeutic massage from a professional practitioner. I was then a teenager, and it was the first time I became aware of the natural healing power and life force within me. That experience pointed me in a new direction, which eventually led me to dedicate my life to shiatsu. I met and studied with Tokujiro Namikoshi, the father of shiatsu, and I was intrigued by his theory about hands-on healing: "Pressing the human body stimulates the fountains of life." It is my goal to continue to follow closely the path shown to me by Tokujiro and his son Toru. Receiving shiatsu makes me healthy, and giving shiatsu also makes me healthy. The teaching of shiatsu-doh is of great significance to me because I live a happy life while making others happy. As I continue to travel along this road, I am grateful for the support and instruction of all my patients, staff, colleagues at home and abroad, and friends and family.

I am very pleased to publish this book in 2003 because it marks an important anniversary: it was 50 years ago that my teacher, Tokujiro Namikoshi sensei, first travelled to the United States, accompanied by his son Toru, to introduce shiatsu outside Japan. Also this year, my mother, Tsugiko, celebrates her 90th birthday. She is a remarkable woman who conquered both tuberculosis and breast cancer in a time when there was almost no hope of surviving them.

ACKNOWLEDGEMENTS

The manuscript upon which I based this book was first compiled by journalist Janice Mawhinney, who had written a story on me and shiatsu for The Toronto Star in 1995. A few years after the story appeared, we arranged for her to conduct a further series of interviews with me, and she organized them into a manuscript. For a long time, it gathered dust, until one day last year I showed it to a patient of mine, Ross Oakes, who is the chaplin of a Catholic high school in Mississauga, Ontario, and who is very enthusiastic about shiatsu. Ross strongly encouraged me to publish it. Starting with the basic skeleton Janice Mawhinney had prepared, I began the time-consuming process of revising the manuscript to turn it into this book. Many people provided help and encouragement along the way. Without their support, the publication of this book would not have been possible. To all who assisted me, I extend my heartfelt gratitude. I can never thank you enough for your encouragement and understanding.

Kensen Saito
July 2003

INTRODUCTION

Throughout the 20th century, our society experienced one technological advance after another, which not only made daily life more convenient but also much more fast paced. The difference between our grandparents' lifestyle just a century ago and ours is staggering. Think of all the machinery, electronics and other devices that have been invented to streamline the way we live. We take for granted our wide-ranging use of them – it only takes a brief power outage to remind us. Through technology and transportation, we have compressed distance and time. This is the legacy of the 20th century.

So, too, have the medical advances of the past century been significant and far-reaching. As an example, we need only point to the many life-saving vaccines and medications that were discovered. But the human race survived thousands of years without them, once relying on more natural therapies. I think we have tipped the scale too far in favour of pharmaceutical approaches. It's time to restore some balance. An American medical study I once read stated that when patients visit their family doctors about a physical ailment, in 70 per cent of the cases the problem is stress related. That's the vast majority of cases! Stress causes imbalance of the body's systems; when the systems don't harmonize, the immune system doesn't function well, so we are susceptible to illness. By acknowledging that most problems stem from stress and by understanding the structure of the body and how it functions, anyone can recognize the benefits of shiatsu. Through the technique of thumb pressure, it restores the body's balance and structure and regulates its functions. Whether there is a deficiency of chemicals or hormones or an excess of them, shiatsu brings their production back to normal. The way of shiatsu is to help the body restore its own physiological balance naturally, instead of treating the symptoms synthetically through medications.

I lived the first 28 years of my life in Japan and then immigrated to Canada, where I have lived for 24 years. I travel to Asia, Europe, the United States and South

America several times a year to be present at international shiatsu congresses and seminars and to practise shiatsu on individuals at such events as the Olympics and film festivals. When I meet people from different countries, no matter what their ethnic background, religion, age, sex or occupation, I hear them say, "I don't want to take medication" and "I want to avoid an operation." As a shiatsu therapist, there are times when I recommend continuing with drug treatment or having an operation. But there are many times when I can recommend shiatsu with confidence; for example, in a particular case, I might ascertain that the patient's health will improve after five shiatsu treatments or, in another case, I may feel the best approach is one treatment a week for three months. We have to be patient and trust in the body's healing abilities. It doesn't always happen overnight. The life force belongs to nature – it has its own rhythms, so we must respect that and give the body the time it needs to heal.

In reflecting on our health care system, I fear we have come to depend too much on medications, and their widespread use has not only produced side effects but also weakened the body's immune system and lowered its natural healing powers. That is why in this century it is very important that we create a new health care system and regain some of our natural healing powers. I would like to see doctors be able to prescribe multidisciplinary approaches for their patients, without feeling pressure from the pharmaceutical industry if that means drugless therapy in certain cases.

Now that we've crossed the threshold into the 21st century, our environment is an increasing cause for concern. Environmental problems exist on a scale much broader than what can be pinpointed city by city, country by country. Problems such as pollution will only be solved through cooperation at a global level. Every day, we are breathing air, drinking water and eating food that is harmful to our body. Some people are starting to realize that taking medication to treat the resulting health problems is a backward approach. To everybody who seeks a natural and safe treatment, whether he or she is a member of the public or a medical professional, I recommend hands-on therapy or, more precisely, the highest level of hands-on therapy: shiatsu. After 30 years of receiving shiatsu treatments myself and treating thousands of others, my goal continues to be to introduce people to the outstanding benefits of this healing art. The reason that shiatsu has spread so far already is that those who have experienced its good effects have convinced others that it is a genuine therapy. If I can make even a few more people aware of the way of shiatsu through the publication of this book and subsequently help them live a healthier life, I will be happy.

CHAPTER 1
THE THUMB-PRESSURE HEALING ART AND ITS ORIGINS

Shiatsu is a truly amazing healing art!

I've witnessed hundreds of people benefit from it. By curing her debilitating back pain, shiatsu allowed rhythmic gymnast Mary Fuzesi to continue training and go on to represent Canada at the Olympic Games in Seoul, where she achieved her best ever performance. It helped Canadian actor Brent Carver excel on Broadway and subsequently win a Tony Award for Best Actor in a Broadway musical. It enabled my mother to catch a cancerous growth in her body; now at the age of 90, about 20 years after breast cancer surgery, she remains in good health. It helped a young lady afflicted with cerebral palsy, who lived the first 18 years of her life on prescription medication, to control her seizures and eventually go off the medication. It revitalized President Havel of the Czech Republic, who was coping with the demands of his career while recovering from the removal of a lung tumour. And singer Anne Murray is convinced shiatsu played a part in lowering her golf score!

What is shiatsu and how can it help?

The word shiatsu literally means "thumb and finger pressure"; in Japanese, shi means "thumbs and fingers," and atsu means "pressure." Through this technique, a trained practitioner presses with the thumbs, fingers and palms on particular pressure points all over the body. Shiatsu is not magic. It is not a New Age spiritual therapy. It has nothing to do with meridian lines. There is nothing occult, mystical or incomprehensible about it. Shiatsu theory is scientifically valid. It works for sound, concrete reasons that can be explained through anatomy and physiology. Shiatsu works where it is needed because it stimulates the body to use its own forces as best it can. It triggers the release of hormones and chemicals necessary to heal, soothe and help the mind and body perform at their peak. It transmits its healing power to different parts of the body through the largest sense organ we have – the skin. This gives it an extraordinary range of applications.

Shiatsu can be especially effective in treating stress-related symptoms and other common medical problems caused by an imbalance of the autonomic nervous system, such as headache, insomnia, hypertension, constipation, diarrhea, asthma, stiff neck and shoulders, menstrual irregularity and back pain. It speeds recovery and rehabilitation after an illness, accident or surgery, such as a stroke, whiplash or a mastectomy. Shiatsu helps to relieve the aches and pains of neuralgia and joint and muscle pain. It promotes relaxation and gives people a wonderful sense of their own body, thereby sharpening concentration. Shiatsu works for people of all ages and at all stages of life. It can soothe an infant and it can ease the pains of an elderly person. I see it every day in my Shiatsu Academy in Toronto.

In this book, I provide background on how the practice of shiatsu developed, how I learned it and how I have been able to use it to help actors, singers, athletes, politicians, lawyers, professors, teachers, students, business executives, homemakers and many, many others. I will also share my insights on how it works, based on more than 30 years of experience. You might find it hard to believe that one technique can have such a wide variety of uses, but I will demonstrate it to be so. Here are a few ways shiatsu helps your body help itself:

- It stimulates your circulation and improves blood flow. This helps reduce blood congestion, helps your organs function better and gives you renewed energy.
- It eases pain and helps heal injuries by improving circulation and stimulating the release of helpful hormones.
- It regulates your nervous system and loosens your muscles, giving you a feeling of well-being; it helps you sleep soundly.
- It encourages the production of natural chemicals in your brain that lift your spirits, and it sharpens your immune system.
- In some way, although we don't yet understand how, it also stimulates creativity. I have seen this again and again in the people who come to me for treatment.

THE THUMB-PRESSURE HEALING ART AND ITS ORIGINS

The importance of touch

Part of shiatsu's effectiveness is skin-to-skin touch. Being touched is a very basic human need that we all too often forget in our mad rush towards bigger and better intellects and smaller and better microchips. Touch is an important kind of communication. We need it to heal and we need it to maintain health. It's a technique I love to work with because it's completely natural. Its benefits come drug-free; it has no side effects (whereas side effects from medication actually make the human body weaker).

When I was 17 and had my first treatment from a professional – a kind of therapeutic massage – I realized immediately that it was different from any medical treatment I had experienced before. It had an impact on me that was unlike all the temperature taking, needles, drugs and other medical interventions I had known until then, and it was accomplished through touch. The skin is the largest organ in the body and has numerous concentrations of sense receptors; the other sense organs are our eyes, nose, ears and tongue. One of the things our sense organs do is to give the brain information about the safety or lack of safety of our body. The receptors in the skin send information through the nervous system to the brain, and the brain feeds back messages about how our body should react. When we feel cold, the information is channelled from our skin through the nervous system to the brain, and the brain sends back a message to try to retain heat.

Shiatsu uses the sense receptors in the skin, muscles, bones and tendons to send messages to the brain, and the brain then decides what should be done. For example, when shiatsu is performed on the front part of the neck and on the abdomen, that particular stimulation turns up the parasympathetic part of the nervous system and induces a relaxed state. Yoga, tai chi and breathing exercises are all useful approaches for helping people relax, but shiatsu is particularly good because it stimulates through direct touch. And one of the effects of relaxation is lower blood pressure. Medical statistics indicate that in North America, the three most prominent causes of death are heart disease, cancer and stroke. High blood pressure often contributes to heart disease and stroke, so hypertension management is very important.

Our society's frenzied pace creates a physical imbalance that pushes blood pressure higher. Our whole society may need to slow down, but until it does, we can learn to gear down as individuals and restore the harmony between our internal rhythm and the rhythm of nature. There is a rhythm to the world around us, which is connected to life's cycles. Everything has a cycle, from the movement of the Earth around the sun to the female menstrual cycle. The body's rhythm is a microcosm of the rhythm of the cosmos, and the two need to harmonize. Shiatsu promotes the balance that makes this possible, as do yoga and meditation. In fact, patients occasionally remark after a shiatsu treatment, "I feel as if I've just had a good meditation." This is one way in which shiatsu is excellent preventive medicine.

Light, smell, sound and touch can either be healing or damaging, depending on how we use them. A good smell makes people relax; the smell of coffee in the morning makes you feel good. But a cold north wind gives people discomfort. Discomfort stimulation makes us tense and, in that state, the brain cannot release the proper healthy chemicals. But when tapped into, the senses can be a bridge to our natural healing systems. When a baby is held by a loving parent, it relaxes in the warmth of the parent's arms. Comfortable, pleasant stimulation through the senses can be the trigger to the healing mechanism. Shiatsu is administered using the hands and the fingertips because they are very sensitive. For a long time, shiatsu practitioners were taught that it worked by affecting two main systems: the circulatory system and the nervous system. Today we know that the brain, the hormones and the immune system are all positively affected by shiatsu. The effect of shiatsu pressure runs through the nervous system to the brain and stimulates the hypothalamus and the pituitary gland on the way. These two are important to hormonal balance; indeed, the pituitary gland is the master of the hormones. Positive stimulation, which is achieved through pressure, triggers it to regulate hormonal secretions. Shiatsu affects other glands of the endocrine system in much the same way – by stimulating the body's production of natural chemicals and creating an energy change in the body. As well, the pressure involved creates a kind of pumping movement that improves circulation.

The man who discovered the healing power of shiatsu

I learned to practise shiatsu from the man who developed it as it is practised today in Japan: Tokujiro Namikoshi. He developed the technique as a child to ease his mother's pain. Tokujiro was born November 3, 1905, into a family with four brothers and sisters. His father had an umbrella business on Shikoku Island, in the southern part of Japan. One year, the weather was so wet and cold that the glue would not dry on the umbrellas in time to meet the deadline of a big order from China, so his father was forced to declare bankruptcy. The family moved to Hokkaido, the northern Japanese island. It was a long, tough trip in late autumn, and the extremely cold, harsh weather was a drastic change from the warm, mild climate they were used to. When they finally reached their destination, they found it to be quite a primitive place: a simple hut with no heat or running water. They settled in as best as they could under the stress-

The master Tokujiro Namikoshi, then 74, with me, then 28, at the Japan Shiatsu School, 1979.

ful circumstances, but soon Tokujiro's mother was suffering terribly from aches and pains in all her joints. She had developed rheumatoid arthritis.

In such a remote area, there was no doctor and nothing could be done for her, so her five children took turns rubbing her sore joints in an effort to ease the discomfort. After a while, she told Tokujiro that his hands were the best at relieving her pain. He took on the job as her physical therapist, while his brothers and sisters divided up the household chores. Eventually, his mother said to him, "When you press instead of rub, I feel much better." So he concentrated on doing that. One day, he was pressing different areas when he came across a point that felt very cold and stiff. He spent some time and effort pressing on it, and his mother said it eased her pain. He continued to press that point daily. The more the hard spot softened under his thumb, the more relief his mother felt and the faster she recovered. Eventually, with the help of Tokujiro's treatment, his mother's rheumatoid arthritis disappeared. She lived into her late 80s in good health.

Up until that time in Japan, massage through stroking or rubbing was widely known, including the Chinese technique called anma, as well as European techniques. Instinctively, human beings have always used the hands to ease pain. When we have a headache, we rub our temples; when we have a stomachache, we rub our abdomen with our palms. Throughout history we can find many examples of the use of the hands to heal. Saints laid their hands on people to perform miracles of healing. Massage was well known in ancient Greece, and for hundreds of years it has been used in India. The innovation developed by Tokujiro Namikoshi was to use the pressure of the thumbs, fingers and palms over the whole body. As a technique, it is significantly different from all the others.

It evidently came naturally to Tokujiro to be a therapist. In his small village, the message spread quickly through word of mouth that this boy was something special. When his mother told a Buddhist monk visiting the village about her son's deeds, the monk became convinced Tokujiro was the reincarnation of a high-ranking monk who had lived years ago and healed many people in his lifetime. When the wife

THE THUMB-PRESSURE HEALING ART AND ITS ORIGINS

of Tokujiro's school principal found that she was unable to produce milk to nurse her newborn baby, the principal asked Tokujiro to help. He used his pressing techniques, and the woman started to produce milk freely for her child. The principal addressed a special school assembly about the wonderful gifts Tokujiro had shared to help his mother and the principal's family, and it made the boy feel proud and happy. He decided at that moment that he would dedicate his life to using the pressing techniques to help people.

The Buddhist monk began to take him on his rounds to visit villagers who were having problems with aches and pains. Tokujiro applied his natural abilities to great success. When Tokujiro was in his late teens, the monk took him to the nearest city, where they planned to try out his skills on city dwellers. Unfortunately, shortly after they arrived, they were arrested by the police for practising without a licence. Tokujiro was held in custody overnight, then headed straight home to his village the next day. After telling his family about the experience, his older brother advised him to go to Tokyo and get a licence to use his techniques.

In those days in Japan, there were only two kinds of manual therapy: a Western-style massage and the ancient Chinese massage technique anma. Tokujiro studied anma under an expert and got his licence for both anma and massage. He then returned to Hokkaido and opened his first clinic in the city of Muroran. However, he offered neither anma nor massage, just the pressing techniques he had developed himself. He pondered what he should call his methods. He came across the word shiatsu in a magazine article referring to finger pressure, and he liked it. Although at the time he was using mostly thumb pressure, in Japanese the thumb and four fingers are all referred to as fingers, so the word shiatsu described very well what he was doing.

As he continued to practise, Tokujiro studied anatomy and physiology and developed a scientific theory to explain how shiatsu works. He came to understand that when he had pressed certain points on his mother's body it had been like giving her natural cortisone shots because he was stimulating her adrenal gland. He knew doctors used cortisone shots effectively to treat joint pain associated with rheumatoid arthritis, for example. When he found out that the body can produce its own cortisone, he couldn't help but wonder why physicians had resorted to using cortisone made by a pharmaceutical company. Other results turned out to have similar scientific explanations. The more he studied and thought, the more he came to believe that the body has everything it needs – it produces all of the chemicals necessary to heal itself. Under stress, the body is put in a state of imbalance and does not produce the right amounts of healthy chemicals. Instead, it can produce destructive substances. Shiatsu can reduce the effects of stress on body and nudge it back towards a healthy state of balance. It was then that Tokujiro chose these words as a slogan for his technique: "The heart of shiatsu is like a mother's love. Pressing the body stimulates the fountains of life." It was a reflection of his attitude of caring and healing.

Tokujiro's fame spreads

When Tokujiro was 25 years old, in the early days of his practice, the famous philosopher Gohei Ishimaru came to Hokkaido by train one day to deliver a lecture to an audience of 2,000, a much anticipated event sponsored by the local newspaper. Ishimaru was in a weakened condition and had to deliver his lectures sitting down instead of standing at a lectern. When he arrived at the Sapporo railway station, he fell and injured himself. He thought he would have to cancel his appearance that night. The sponsors from the newspaper were in a panic. One writer had heard about Tokujiro Namikoshi's reputation, so they called on him for help. He went to the inn where the philosopher was staying and treated him until he appeared to be much better. Instead of cancelling, Ishimaru made a two-hour speech – standing up! He himself was amazed at his heightened physical strength and well-being. "Your thumbs are very precious," he said to Tokujiro. "I want to insure them." He insured Tokujiro's thumbs for 100,000 yen – that's the equivalent of $10 million today! The story made the national newspaper.

Ishimaru counselled Tokujiro that if he wanted to spread the word about shiatsu nationwide he should practise in Tokyo, where many people from all walks of life could benefit from it. By that time, Tokujiro was married and had children, but he took the philosopher's advice, gave his Hokkaido clinic to a relative and moved his family to Tokyo. Ishimaru introduced him to many influential people, but shiatsu was so new and unknown that it took many years before Tokujiro successfully established and expanded his practice. He had to move seven times, usually because he could not pay the rent. When he moved for the eighth time, he told himself, "This is where I stay, fail or succeed. I won't move again!" His shiatsu college is still in that very place today. It is where I myself studied.

In his early years of practice, Tokujiro did mostly house calls and was limited to helping seven or eight people a day. But because he had come to Tokyo to spread the practice of his methods, he decided to start teaching. In 1940, he established his school and began to train shiatsu practitioners. Eventually, they approached the government to ask it to legally recognize shiatsu. After the Second World War, the American general Douglas McArthur directed the Japanese health ministry for some years. There were more than 300 unregulated therapies in Japan at the time, so McArthur ordered scientists at the universities to research all of them and document which ones had scientific proof of merit and which did not. At the end of the eight years, the universities reported back that shiatsu was the only therapy backed up by scientific research. In 1955, the Japanese health ministry legally recognized shiatsu and it became a licensed therapy. Unfortunately, massage, shiatsu and traditional anma massage all come under one licence in Japan, which is very confusing for people; that also means that people who get a licence in one of the other therapies can hang out a shiatsu sign when they really have no shiatsu training at all.

It's all in the hands

Tokujiro was not a big man, but his thumbs were very large and soft. When one practises shiatsu every day, the balls of the thumbs and fingers get really soft. This is good because they need to be extremely sensitive to pick up messages from the patient's body. I have often wondered what our fingerprints are for. Why do we have those little swirls on our fingertips? I know that our skin breathes, but there is more being transmitted through the skin than gases; there is a transfer of energy.

The human hand is a wonderful thing. It is the most sensitive part of the body. There are many sense receptors in the balls of the thumbs and fingers and in the palms. It is important that shiatsu not be done using any mechanical devices, only the hands. When a shiatsu therapist finds a point of complex tightness, pushing with a stick or other instrument would not be useful, and elbow pressure would not work to ease it either. Our thumbs and hands are sensitive and precise enough to do exactly what is needed; they can work out the knots in little muscles one by one. For best results, the patient needs to be relaxed. A trained shiatsu practitioner's hands have warmth, and applying the proper amount of pressure can keep the patient relaxed. It is only the hands that can do this. The amount of pressure - gentle but deep - has to be comfortable for both patient and practitioner. Nothing should be forced.

Shiatsu is truly an art, so it took me seven years to develop the feel for just the right level of pressure in exactly the right place. If the pressure is too strong, it is uncomfortable. If it is too soft, it does not work. There are many important nerves and arteries running through our whole body. Pressing on the right point will stimulate production of the appropriate chemicals, and these chemical changes in the body make you feel good. It can be similar to the state of a good meditation or a "runner's high." Feeling relaxed is essential for health and recovery. Research shows that when people relax, their immune systems become stronger. That's why shiatsu can be key in a preventive health regimen.

The long-term value of shiatsu

When an individual is under a great deal of stress, such as during a divorce or when there is a death in the family, his or her immune function is lowered. The cardiovascular system is affected, so the person is prone to high blood pressure. He or she proba-

THE THUMB-PRESSURE HEALING ART AND ITS ORIGINS

bly has more digestive and stomach problems and is more at risk of becoming ill. Stress and discomfort are the complete opposite of that good, relaxed feeling that is the key to a healthy body. The body has its own power to heal, but when stress disrupts normal functioning, it does not produce enough of the natural substances needed for homeostasis. Shiatsu restores normal production.

I am in my 50s, and because I lead such a hectic life, I need a shiatsu treatment every two weeks if I can possibly manage to spare the time. I always aim for a treatment once a week, but if I happen to miss two weeks in a row I really feel it. That comes to about 25 shiatsu treatments a year; it would cost a person about $1,500 a year for that. Seems like a lot? Well, consider how many hundreds of dollars a year some people spend on high blood pressure medication alone. Shiatsu makes sound economic sense. Of course, it cannot replace all drugs, but it could replace some, hypertension medication among the first.

I've seen many patients benefit both healthwise and financially from shiatsu. I recall the time a mother brought her grown son to see me after his doctor told them he needed knee surgery as soon as possible. After one treatment, his pain was completely gone; he did not have to go through with the surgery. If he had, his mother would have been burdened with the fee for surgery, hospital charges and rehabilitation costs. Also, the young man would have had to give up his job because he was going to be off recovering for so long. The value of shiatsu became very clear to them.

Promoting good circulation

Many illnesses are related to problems in the circulatory system; shiatsu promotes good circulation. The billions of cells in our body need sufficient oxygen and nutrients to live, thrive and fulfill all their normal functions. Whether, and how, each cell receives what it needs all depends on the circulatory system. If each cell is healthy – if you are healthy on the cellular level – then the body is healthy. Strokes and heart attacks are mainly a result of arteries or capillaries rupturing, clotting or being plugged by plaque. That is why diet is so important, and why smoking is so damaging. The blockage can prevent the cells from receiving enough oxygen and nutrients. In fact, 20 per cent of the oxygen we take in is required by our brain, so if the supply is blocked, it is very dangerous. Some of my students give shiatsu treatments at a stroke recovery centre in downtown Toronto. In the case of a stroke, the more time that passes before any rehabilitative treatment is begun, the less likely it is that the patient can be helped in a significant way. But if started early after the stroke, shiatsu can be very beneficial. I would like to see shiatsu incorporated into rehabilitation programs more and more – not only in the case of stroke but for all post-operative recovery. Financing is an issue since stroke victims often cannot continue at their jobs. But we must find a way, perhaps through referral by the patient's physician so that the therapy would be covered by health insurance.

Cerebral palsy

Similarly, shiatsu can be beneficial to children with cerebral palsy. Just as it is only in the very early stages after a stroke that shiatsu can make any real difference, so it is true of the early stages of cerebral palsy. Once a brain cell is damaged, it never recovers, but perhaps it is possible for bypasses to be formed between live cells during infancy, when the brain is in a phenomenal period of development. Every day, the child needs touch because touch stimulates neuron development in the brain. With shiatsu, we send an enormous amount of information to the cerebrum. I had an 18-year-old patient with cerebral palsy who came regularly for treatments. Until she was six or seven, her mother massaged her daily, which was clearly helpful. She still took strong medications to ward off epileptic seizures, but after she started coming to me regularly, she was able to decrease her medication, and two years later was able to do without it altogether.

Clinical successes and research opportunities

We think we know a lot about the human body, but there are still so many unknowns about how it functions. During the 20th century, there were many great medical

THE THUMB-PRESSURE HEALING ART AND ITS ORIGINS

advances, such as the discovery of insulin and cortisone. The brain is a hot topic right now, and I am hopeful that the more research we do on it, the more we will understand how shiatsu benefits its functioning. The benefits are often difficult to pinpoint. For example, I've given a series of treatments to patients with Parkinson's disease, and each person's condition has either stabilized or improved as a result. We cannot see from the outside exactly what changes have taken place inside to produce those results. One hypothesis is that shiatsu stimulates the production of dopamine, which is lacking in people with Parkinson's.

When it comes to reversing infertility, I have had many clinical successes. Most women who come to my clinic because they are unable to conceive do become pregnant after several months of shiatsu. It is my hope that the medical community will someday consider undertaking joint research on infertility and the role of shiatsu. I would welcome such collaborative efforts. A few years ago, researchers studying multiple sclerosis and hands-on therapy at a Toronto hospital approached me about a study project after learning that many patients found shiatsu helpful. In the end, the study didn't go ahead because of insufficient funding but, still, I considered it a step in the right direction.

The body's natural healing power

Tokujiro felt that modern society depends far too much on medications and surgery. Through shiatsu, it is possible for a person to develop tremendous health and strength, he said, because shiatsu stimulates the body to work at healing itself. It is like a switch that turns on the body's own healing power.

I, too, believe we need to concentrate more on stimulating the body's natural healing power. These days, we focus so much on drugs and surgery in our search for "health care" that we get "sick care" instead. We need to turn to preventive techniques like shiatsu rather than wait until someone is sick and then address the problem. An extensive study done in Montreal by the Canadian government found that the most efficient way to spend cancer-fighting dollars is to educate people on how to avoid getting cancer in the first place. We need to look at making good nutrition, yoga and shiatsu priorities in our lives. I wish medical schools would teach doctors the effectiveness of these preventive approaches in addition to teaching them to administer medication. Nowadays, people are looking for other therapies, but because physicians aren't taught about them, more and more people are supplementing their doctor visits by consulting naturopaths and exploring forms of natural healing. In their quest to improve their own health, people have been educating themselves about healthy lifestyles and taking steps to improve their diet and get regular exercise. Shiatsu fits well into this trend. Like aromatherapy, light therapy (for those with Seasonal Affective Disorder), acupuncture, massage and other therapies, shiatsu takes advantage of the body's sense receptors to send signals of health through the nervous system to the brain. It is my hope that our society will start dedicating more money, education and energy to preventive health care so that the next generation will have the opportunity to draw on the best of both conventional medicine and other approaches to health care. Shiatsu is sometimes referred to as an "alternative therapy" or an "Eastern therapy." I do not like these categories because I don't feel "Eastern," "Western" and "alternative" are helpful terms in describing an approach to health care. What is important is whether the approach is natural or not.

Shiatsu and cancer

Sometimes during treatments, my thumbs will detect a tumour, and I urge the patient in question to be examined by a doctor. These tumours are not always malignant, but when they are, often the cancer is too far advanced for there to be much hope. Even when the outlook is not good, these patients always tell me they appreciated the fact that I found the tumour. One person said to me, "I now know how many days I have to live, so I thank you for finding the tumour."

One day, I found a tumour on my mother's armpit. She had it examined and was told she had breast cancer. She had surgery and started undergoing chemotherapy, but after three-quarters of the treatments she decided not to continue because the reactions were too much for her. She had already modified her diet and was doing tai chi regularly, so she continued to focus on healthy eating and exercise. Needless to say, she also continued having shiatsu treatments at least once every two weeks. It has now been 20 years since her surgery, and this year she celebrates her 90th birthday.

People often ask whether shiatsu can fight cancer or AIDS. I always try to explain that shiatsu is not a focus on any one illness. Its focus is on one's inner life force, which has unlimited healing powers. People need to have hope and encouragement. Shiatsu can prevent illness and it can restore our body to its normal functioning. When our body is in a healthy state, our immune system can prevent disease. In the case of cancer, shiatsu can be an effective way to detect it at an early stage, and if caught early, the prognosis is often good. Shiatsu promotes self-awareness; through regular treatments, we become more attuned to our body. So when we sense something is wrong, that's our body's own health barometer pointing out the area that needs attention and thus promoting its own health. This is not magic; it is science.

Furthermore, illness can be a wake-up call that it's time to change our bad habits and reduce the stress to which we subject ourselves. I encourage ill patients to consider the recovery period precious time to rest and reflect on their life and its purpose. Seeing things in a positive light promotes the healing that comes from within. In the case of cancer, I feel the most important factors in the chance for recovery are a good surgeon, a positive lifestyle change and a support network of family and friends.

In touch with nature

Metabolic problems such as diabetes and high cholesterol can take a long time to improve through a combination of shiatsu and lifestyle changes, but locomotive problems such as whiplash, car accident injuries, carpal tunnel syndrome and industrial injuries can be treated more quickly. Energy in the body is an interesting thing to consider. In my clinical experience, the muscles and joints of a professional electrician are different from those of other people. Sometimes they are numb, and sometimes there are aches and pains, but they are definitely different. In this age of computers, almost everyone – from young children to office workers – spends a third of his or her day touching an electrical system. Not only can people get carpal tunnel syndrome from repetitive motion, but they are also touching electrical devices from six to eight hours a day. There is no way the nervous system can avoid being affected by this; the body was not meant to be in contact with electricity every day. I believe it would be good for people to spend an hour a day gardening, touching the soil – literally getting in touch with nature. We do not usually touch nature, especially if we live in the city. But think how revitalizing a holiday by the sea is. That's because soaking in salt water is healthy; it's a natural treatment. Shiatsu is also a natural treatment, and it helps put us in touch with natural rhythms. All the natural cycles in our world – day and night, the tides, our heartbeat, women's menstrual cycles and so on – are part of the rhythms of life. When we are not in harmony with them, the balance needs to be restored.

Rethinking health care

Tokujiro did not talk about meridian lines. He insisted that shiatsu theory had to be scientifically valid. He found the explanation in the body's production of endorphins and other hormones. The body produces chemicals at levels that are not harmful. Shiatsu normalizes the function of the organs and the production of these chemicals. It never has damaging side effects because it does not encompass anything unnatural. If someone is constipated or afflicted with an intestinal disorder, a colonic irrigation may be appropriate in an emergency situation, but it is not natural. It is better to address the problem by eating properly to cleanse the system. In days gone by, certain foods and drinks were consumed in order to cleanse the body, but we have moved to a reliance on unnatural substances to treat physical problems.

I would like to see a system develop in which medical problems are assessed case by case; that is, health care practitioners would decide which person should be operated on for a heart defect and which person might be able to recover more naturally. I would also like to see many more health care workers of all specialties learn to administer shiatsu treatments. For example, they would find these skills useful in working with senior citizens, addressing cases of whiplash or industrial injuries and treating carpal tunnel syndrome in the workplace. Midwives could use shiatsu to ease patients' morning sickness, swollen joints, back pain and labour pains. I believe that shiatsu can be useful in a variety of fields and that anyone can benefit from learning it. It is simple, inexpensive and effective. Besides, both giving and receiving a shiatsu treatment is a way of getting to know another person and to learn more about yourself – both participants get something out of it.

Improving mental acuity

Not only can shiatsu relieve our aches and pains and keep our body attuned to a healthy, natural rhythm but it can also improve mental clarity and focus. Human skin can sense temperature, pressure and pleasure; these mixed sensations travel to the thalamus and to the limbic system, the command centre for physical appetites and instincts. With shiatsu, the message about sensation travels at a subconscious level to the limbic system, then continues to the cerebral cortex, where it gets conscious recognition. Even before it reaches the conscious level, the message influences the body by triggering a neuro-endocrine chain reaction. Shiatsu has a very powerful effect on the endocrine, or hormonal, system. The pressure used is deep, so the body receives messages through muscles, tendons, ligaments and sometimes even the bones. The message ends up in the cerebellum, the centre of neuromuscular coordination, so that function is also improved.

Shiatsu's chain reaction helps the body heal itself and triggers it to regenerate its systems. How wonderful it is that hand therapy – without the use of any expensive medications or complex machines – can boost an individual's healing, alertness and creativity!

A LAUGH REJUVENATES.
A FROWN AGES

一笑一若
一怒一老

CHAPTER 2

SHIATSU
AT EVERY STAGE
OF LIFE

At the beginning of our lives, we need touch. Being held and touched by our parents sustains us. It is just as essential that we be held and touched at the end of our lives, if at all possible. All people, from infants to centenarians, can benefit from the touch inherent in the technique of shiatsu.

Shiatsu and children

Toru Namikoshi's son Takashi was born prematurely. Toru gave him shiatsu treatments and he eventually grew strong and healthy, developing normally in spite of his early arrival and low birth weight. Because of this experience, Toru often recommended shiatsu for babies.

In my own practice, I have given treatments to many children and teens, and sometimes to babies and elementary schoolchildren. I adjust the amount of pressure to suit the age and size of the person, so I use much less pressure on a baby than I would on someone older. Infancy is a vital time for brain development, so the focus of my work with babies is full-body shiatsu to stimulate their sense receptors and to try to maximize their body's ability to send messages to the brain. There is a connection between the skin and the brain from the embryonic stage of life. Communicating with a baby through touch is very important because that's how they learn. The very young use their lips and hands to explore new things, thereby gathering information about the world around them. That is why it is good to encourage this development in the early stages of life. Shiatsu is a particularly effective way of doing so because it stimulates the whole body through human touch. It also strengthens a baby's immune system. In fact, I notice that shiatsu offers a kind of protection for patients of all ages. My gymnast patients seem to get fewer injuries than their colleagues, and over the years I have observed that regular patients are less prone to physical fatigue. Since accidents are more likely to occur when concentration is poor, shiatsu can play a part in preventing them by sharpening focus and concentration. It also extends energy, something we can all benefit from at any age. That's why I started giving treatments to my daughters, nieces and nephews in infancy and, as they grew older, I also taught them to use their fingers, palms and thumbs to stimulate different pressure points on their own body.

Even elementary schoolchildren feel a lot of pressure and uncertainty in their lives these days. They face school stresses, peer pressure and sometimes family problems as well. They aren't yet clear about what direction their life will take and they worry about that. Shiatsu can be calming and helpful for children going through this phase. It can help them focus on their schoolwork and sustain the energy needed for sports and other activities.

Shiatsu and teens

Life can be even more stressful in the teen years. The body's hormonal balance is changing and causing physical stresses, which affect emotional balance. Teens' bodies grow and develop at a sometimes surprisingly fast rate, which often makes them uncomfortable. No longer children protected by parents and teachers, but not yet adults completely responsible for themselves, for a few years they are caught in an awkward place in the middle. They often want to be treated as adults but they don't yet have the experience, maturity and judgement. At school, their studies are challenging. Financially, they are not yet independent. This all leads to feelings of frustration for many of them, and they are often injury-prone from all the pressure and stress in their lives. Virtually every teen could benefit from regular shiatsu treatments to reduce stress levels; for example, having a treatment the day before an exam can help concentration a great deal. It is very important for adults to teach teens how to get rid of their stress in positive ways so that they don't turn to smoking, drinking and drugs.

Shiatsu can provide significant preventive health benefits to young people, especially young women, who may be vulnerable to scoliosis, a curving of the spine. Eighty per cent of the people who develop this condition are female. Its cause is not clear. Having regular shiatsu treatments starting in the early teen years can loosen the ligaments, tendons and muscles so that the range of any potential curvature of the spine is lessened.

Both skeletal and muscular development can be enhanced through shiatsu, so young athletes in training benefit greatly from it. For young people whose interests lie more in music, art and other cultural pursuits, I recommend shiatsu to enhance their ability to focus. My nieces and nephews, who have had treatments since they were young, are good examples. One of my nieces, who graduated from the University of Toronto and went on to study midwifery, always found that shiatsu helped her relax before an exam. My nephew, a student at the University of British Columbia who is an avid soccer player, has relied on shiatsu to fight fatigue during tournaments.

Shiatsu and adults

Our body continues to grow until about the age of 25. After that, each person ages differently. Some people feel old by 30; others only feel middle-aged at 70 or even 80. A positive outlook in life is the key to feeling young, but under stress and pressure, people tend to close up and drift into a negative state. Shiatsu helps open them up again and brings them to a relaxed, positive state. I notice that the hands often reflect the state of the brain; if the brain gets stiff, the hands get stiff. A fist reflects tension, whereas an open hand reflects relaxation. If the brain is relaxed, then the hands open naturally.

The centre of our being is directly connected to the rhythm of nature. If they are out of sync, then everything else is out of balance. Think about how good you feel at the beach, lulled by the rhythm of the waves breaking along the shore. That's because the rhythms of nature are soothing to us. We feel better in the mountains and in the woodlands. Shiatsu draws on natural rhythms, so it can help a person reconnect with them. Life roars along at a very fast pace and is particularly relentless in the city, making it a physiological challenge for the nervous system to maintain a state of balance. That pace, coupled with regular consumption of coffee and other stimulants, means a lot of adults never relax at all. And that has a detrimental effect on blood pressure and heart rate.

A century ago, the pace of life was much slower and religion was a core of daily life. Religion can harmonize daily routine, provide meaning and purpose to life and teach us to love one another. In our modern society, people take little or no time to go to the temple or to church, to look into themselves or to come face to face with their own lives. Sharing with others, not money and material things, is the key to spiritual well-being. A spiritual connection is what gives meaning and peace.

Because of diseases like AIDS, people have a heightened awareness about how germs and infections can be transmitted through touch or the exchange of fluids. Because they are so on guard, they rarely think of the good things can also be transferred through touch – like comfort and relaxation. As I give a shiatsu treatment, I press on a range of pressure points, including various veins and arteries. I feel the patient's pulse; if it is too rapid or too strong, I focus on that area. By the end of the treatment, the pulse has slowed. As I said earlier, controlling hypertension is very important to ward off the risk of stroke and heart attack, and shiatsu can play an important role. Patients at risk also need to watch their diet, and it is part of my job to educate them. If we look after our health throughout our lives, then our senior years are more likely to be healthy and enjoyable. As baby boomers move into late middle age, it is a critical time for their health. Treating the body well now will pay dividends for years to come.

Shiatsu and women

Women can benefit from shiatsu throughout their lives. Because it helps restore hormonal balance, it can regulate menstrual cycles and help a woman get pregnant if she is having difficulty. Because it has been a successful approach for many of my clients, I strongly recommend regular shiatsu for women having trouble conceiving.

About 60 per cent of my clients are women. Because a woman's health is governed so much by her cycle, irregularity of that cycle can lead to many problems. Imbalance caused by any number of factors, including physical and mental stress and nutritional deficiencies, leads to hormonal imbalance. This snowballs into a number of problems, from menstrual pain to infertility. I have helped several women overcome infertility through regular shiatsu, and others who had suffered severe menstrual pain for 20 or 30 years are no longer afflicted with it.

During pregnancy, shiatsu helps ease back pain and restores good circulation to mitigate swelling from water retention. There are even benefits for the baby in the womb because the mother relaxes so completely and feels so good. The late Denis Binks, a colleague of mine in the Netherlands, was often part of the delivery room team, keeping the mother as relaxed as possible throughout labour and delivery. That made a lot of sense to me, and I have always felt that it would be very useful for nurses and midwives to learn to administer shiatsu treatments. I also recommend a shiatsu treatment for the mother after the baby is born because delivery is hard work. This is especially important to help the body heal after a difficult birth or a birth by Caesarean section. Also, if it becomes apparent in the days after birth that the mother is not producing enough milk, shiatsu can help by restoring hormonal balance, which will stimulate adequate milk production.

Shiatsu and seniors

As Canada's population ages, I would like to see more young people being trained in shiatsu as part of the approach to caring for the elderly. In my experience, the senior members of our society have a profound wisdom to share as a result of their experiences, and it is a precious gift that should be passed on to the younger generation. Unfortunately, the aged are often isolated in our society. I believe shiatsu could serve as a healthy communication bridge between generations, by bringing young health care therapists together with older patients.

I suggest that instead of subsidizing the cost of medications for seniors the government should provide them with 10 paid shiatsu treatments each year. What better way to give something back to our senior citizens, who have contributed so much to our society and paid taxes for so many years?

With aging comes a loss in the acuity of the senses as some of the brain cells start dying. That's why it is important that seniors continue to be touched when

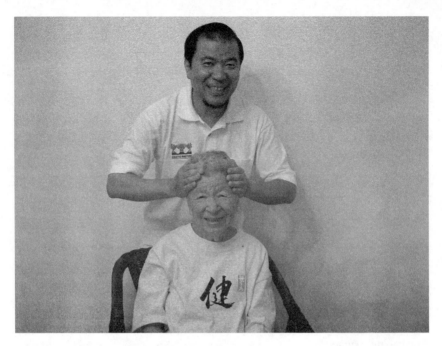

My mother, Tsugiko, age 88, and I, 2002.

they get old: shiatsu's stimulation sends messages to the brain to help keep it functioning sharply. When you meet someone 80 or 90 years old whose brain obviously functions well, usually you find out that the person is active in some particular creative activity such as painting, knitting or playing a musical instrument. They are constantly stimulating their brain. So, too, can regular shiatsu help keep us sharp and vigorous as we age. It energizes us, stimulating the nerves through the sense organs.

I have a patient in her late 80s who once told me she was glad she injured her arm 12 years ago because it led her to start shiatsu treatments. Now she comes for a monthly treatment because she feels it keeps her system limbered up and her energy level high. She even walks up and down a long, steep hill in Toronto's Don Valley every week for exercise, something very few people approaching 90 would consider.

Aging is bound to bring physical limitations, joint stiffness and other discomforts, as well as some chronic health problems. It is always better to focus on what is improving than on what still hurts. There is no point in our lives when we cannot improve our health in some way through regular shiatsu treatments, from before birth right up until death.

HAVING ONCE MADE UP HIS MIND,

A MAN WILL NOT RETURN HOME UNTIL

HIS LEARNING IS COMPLETE

NO ONE KNOWS WHEN DEATH WILL COME

AND HE MAY NOT BE BURIED

IN HIS NATIVE COUNTRY

WHEREVER YOU ARE,

THAT LAND IS YOUR HOME

男兒立志出鄉關
學若無成不復還
埋骨何須桑梓地
人生到處有青山

CHAPTER 3
FROM TOKYO TO TORONTO: MY STORY

Today, I feel that my life is only partly my own. The rest belongs to shiatsu, to all the people I help through shiatsu and to the people I teach to practise it. When I was young, such a statement about my life would have been totally unimaginable to me. The greatest future I could have dreamed up was to be an Olympic medal–winning athlete. Sometimes when I look back and see how I got from that point to this, I am quite astonished.

My parents met a few years before the Second World War, at the Tokyo English Speaking Society. My father was a college student studying English at Tokyo Shodai, and my mother, who had been raised and educated in Canada, had just graduated from the University of British Columbia and moved back to Japan. They married, and when my father returned from serving in the war, they settled in Ichikawa City, near Tokyo, and he started a business. Then I was born on January 27, 1951. I was the second child; I have an older sister. When I was five years old, we moved to Tokyo. The period right after that was not a good one: my father's business went under, he lost his inheritance through gambling, and within a couple of years my parents were divorced. My sister and I were raised by our mother. Mother was always a very hard-working woman and had a positive outlook. From the time I was very young, she let me know that she wanted me to have a good education but that there was more to life than school. "High marks are no guarantee of success in life," she would say. From her, I also learned tolerance and endurance.

The struggle to balance athletics and schoolwork

Judo is very popular in Japan, and as a boy I took judo classes. However, when I was 14, the 1964 Olympic Games in Tokyo changed my interests. The number one Japanese heavyweight judo competitor was defeated by a Dutchman. As well, the Ethiopian Abebe Bikila, a gold medallist at the Rome Olympics, won the marathon for the second time, and a Japanese runner came third (Japan's first track and field medal of the Games). My future course seemed obvious to me: the next day I switched from judo to distance running. Throughout high school, I was so involved with running that my grades got lower with every test. I had entered high school with the second highest marks among all 450 students. By the third year, I was almost at the bottom of the class. I wanted to get into a good university, but with the marks I was getting, the whole idea seemed pretty farfetched. When I had a one-on-one staff-student interview in my third year of high school, the teacher conducting the interview asked me what plans I had for my future. I named a couple of good universities; he laughed and advised me that my academic plans would be virtually impossible with the marks I was getting.

A back injury leads to the discovery of therapeutic massage

I cared very much about becoming an Olympic athlete. I trained hard. One day during gym class, I jumped into the swimming pool and hit my back hard against the water. After that, I suffered terrible back pain. The painkillers my family doctor gave me were no help. The chiropractor I went to was not able to do much. I was in a lot of pain, and it frustrated me that the pain, stiffness, headaches and fatigue were affecting my training.

Finally, a family friend sent me to her practitioner, an old man with a black belt in judo; he was a bone setter. The old man gave me hands-on treatments for 10 or 15 minutes at a time. I was very sore and found the first sessions somewhat painful. But even after the very first treatment, I noticed a difference just walking back to the train station. It felt as if a rope that had been binding me was cut off. My instinct told me that this was different from any treatment I'd had before and was going to help me a great deal. Many of my first-time clients experience the same type of feeling.

I went to the old man for treatments almost every day for a month and a half, and by the end of that time, my symptoms were gone. He asked me what I wanted to do with my life. I told him I was thinking of becoming a journalist and going abroad but first I had to go to a good university, which would be a problem because my marks were so poor. "That's because of the stiffness in your neck," he replied to my surprise. "It keeps you from having the power of concentration." The hands-on treatments he gave me not only removed the problems I'd been having with my back and fatigue but they also released the stiffness in my neck. I did find it easier to concentrate, and my marks began to improve. The old man suggested that I become a physical practitioner like him, but I was not interested at that time. I had other dreams.

That fall, after completing the treatments, I ran in competitions and achieved my best results ever. It was very satisfying. That was a difficult year in Japan, with a lot of conflict between students and police, student demonstrations and pervasive disruption arising out of the student power movement and the resistance to it from authorities. Tear gas was used widely during the demonstrations; sometimes I could not walk up our street without tears in my eyes because of it. The University of Tokyo's entrance exam was cancelled because students had taken over the buildings in protest. Along with many high school graduates that year, I decided to bypass the disruptions, take a year off from my formal studies and prepare for the university entrance exams the following year. A year later, I entered Keio University, the oldest private university in Japan and one of the best in the country.

I could see that I was never going to make it as a distance runner and decided to try out for boxing at the university. One look at the toothless grin of the boxing team's sophomore made me change my mind in a hurry. I signed up for the wrestling team instead. That year, I went periodically for treatments from the old judo man who had helped me recover from my back pain and neck problems. I always went to him before my exams and before my wrestling matches and, with his help, achieved good results. At that time, shiatsu was becoming very popular in Japan, and Tokujiro Namikoshi had a regular television series. I asked the old judo man what he thought of shiatsu. He told me he thought it was very good, so I decided I wanted to learn it. He taught me some of his techniques, and I took an evening course for beginners at the Japan Shiatsu School. I practised on my wrestling teammates and on some family friends who wanted to give it a try.

My sister, Naomi, and I in Times Square, New York, during my first visit to North America, 1972.

Exploring North America

After I finished my second year at university, I took all my savings and travelled through North America for the summer break. My travelling companion was an American man several years older than me; I had first met him when I was in Grade 8. I remember well the clean-shaven GI with a crew cut who came to visit our family during his shore leave in Tokyo on the way to the Vietnam War. He was from a naval family in Minnesota. When he met me at the San Francisco airport, the clean-cut soldier, to my amazement, had turned into a complete hippie with long hair, jeans and a bandana. We travelled across the country in his van, stopping often to pick up hitchhikers who traded marijuana for rides. I did not understand their hippie jargon very well. I was quite put off by all the drugs, and the whole hippie culture was confusing and alien to me. In Japan, I had been raised with a strong work ethic. I could not understand these young people I encountered everywhere we travelled who had no future plans beyond the next joint and who begged for money on the street with no thought of making any contribution to society. It struck me as a kind of social illness.

While that trip was not a happy experience for me, it did leave me with some important impressions. I saw Toronto for the first time when I visited my sister, who lived there already and worked as a waitress for a mere $60 a week. Even though it was only $20 more than she would have received on unemployment insurance, she preferred to do that rather than do nothing. Compared with Tokyo, I found Toronto very attractive because it was spacious, with cleaner air and lots of trees and parks. During that visit, I offered some shiatsu treatments, and people really seemed to like them. One was my future brother-in-law, who ran a successful pizzeria in the Yorkville district of the city. He was suffering from neck pain as the result of a car accident. The people I treated encouraged me to come back to Toronto and continue with shiatsu, but at that time it was only a small part of my life. After leaving Toronto, I travelled west alone by bus and was very impressed by the country I saw through the window; the Canadian Rockies were the most beautiful sight I had experienced in all my travels. I liked Canada and its natural areas very much. I felt I wanted to come back someday.

The search for a fulfilling career

I flew back to Japan in September, returned to university and graduated a year and a half later. Then I took a job with a big company whose head office is in Kyoto. While my classmates all chose companies with very traditional and conservative values, I chose one with an imaginative president who was on the verge of expanding into other countries. Since I wanted to go abroad, this seemed promising to me. The president was a visionary. He had noticed that Western fashions had begun to catch on after the Second World War. Historically, Japanese women had always worn kimonos without underwear, but he decided to tap into the Western influence and establish a women's lingerie company. It was a huge success, and when I started at the company, there were factories in Taiwan, Korea and Thailand as well as the Japan headquarters.

Every day began with employee exercises, a talk on a particular subject and the singing of the company song. Whenever it was my turn to make a presentation, I always did shiatsu. I also did a lot of shiatsu treatments on company executives. I worked hard at my job – 8 a.m. to 11 p.m. – but eventually became very frustrated. I had come to that company to get work outside of Japan but instead I was spending 15 hours a day in Kyoto counting the containers that came in and sorting through piles of underwear to determine the quality of the sewing and dyeing. After a year, I asked when I could go abroad and was told that it wouldn't be for about six years, not until I had thoroughly learned the work in every department in Kyoto. I was 24 years old; six years sounded like forever. So I went to the company president and explained to him that I had to leave. He counselled me that whatever career I intended to pursue, I should build a solid foundation by the age of 30, and that piece of advice really struck me.

During the time that I was trying to determine what I wanted to do with the rest of my life, I received a letter from my sister in Toronto. She was worried about my future and wondered why I didn't consider taking up shiatsu professionally. I had always thought of shiatsu more as an art or a sideline than an occupation, but my sister's suggestion sounded like a good one.

Shiatsu studies

By then I was 25, and although two years of specialized training seemed like a long time on top of the four years I had already completed at university, I enrolled in Tokyo's Japan Shiatsu School, which was headed by Tokujiro Namikoshi. For two years, I studied shiatsu from morning to afternoon, then washed dishes and waited on tables at a restaurant each night until 11:30 p.m. to earn my tuition. My plan was to finish my training, then go to Canada to introduce shiatsu there as a licensed Japanese shiatsu therapist. I took my visa application and immigration papers to the Canadian embassy in Tokyo and explained that I was seeking landed immigrant status. The official who interviewed me asked how I planned to support myself, and I

Tokujiro sensei giving me a shiatsu treatment during a special workshop for graduates at the Japan Shiatsu School, 1979.

explained that I wanted to introduce and practise shiatsu in Canada. He consulted the list of what skills Canada was looking for in immigrants. Shiatsu practitioner was not on the list - in fact, the practice was completely unknown in Canada. I had no chance, he told me. I asked him how I could get to Canada. He said Canada needed computer programmers and Japanese chefs; if I qualified for one of those professions, I could immigrate. For the next six months, I continued my shiatsu training during the day and went to cooking school in the evenings. Finally, I had a chef's licence as well as my shiatsu diploma and shiatsu licence. I received permission to immigrate, and my sister and brother-in-law agreed to sponsor me.

The move to Canada

I arrived in Canada June 6, 1979, clutching all my worldly possessions: a Sony television, a little grill and $1,100. I was 28 years old and full of dreams and illusions. For the first three months, I lived in my sister's basement and took English lessons. The only income I earned during that time was one day of clerical work for $3 an hour. I was offered a chef's job in a Japanese restaurant but I knew if I took it I would not be able to practise shiatsu, so I declined. I decided to try to get a licence to practise drugless therapy in Canada. When I learned that it would take four years to earn my qualifications in chiropractic or physiotherapy but only one year for massage, the choice was obvious. When I presented my documents and explained my experience to the board of directors of the masseurs' organization, they agreed that I had a good enough background to be a masseur and said all I had to do was sit for the exam. But when I saw a copy of an old exam, my heart sank. I knew all the anatomy, physiology and pathology necessary, but my English was not good enough to understand the wording of the questions! One question said, "Define the following pathological conditions." I did not know the meaning of the words define and pathological.

I feared that it would take me four or five years to learn the English terminology I needed to pass the exams. But I knew I had to strike while the iron was hot, so I set to work with a dictionary and applied myself ferociously to memorizing technical terms. Six months later, in March, I passed five of the seven exams. The following September, I passed the other two and became a registered massage therapist in Ontario. After spending a decade of my life writing high school and university exams, company exams, shiatsu exams, cooking licence exams and Ontario massage board exams, I promised myself that was the end of exams for me. Whatever happened, I had to go ahead with the qualifications I already had.

My first clinic

I was 29 years old and ready to work. I got a part-time job at a shiatsu studio in downtown Toronto to support myself while I was studying. On March 14, 1981, just after I turned 30, I opened my own shiatsu clinic called Shiatsu Dohjoh, on Broadview near Danforth Avenue in Toronto. I had a couple of patients lined up, but business built up very slowly. Sometimes I was hired to do treatments at the homes of wealthy residents of the Forest Hill neighbourhood, but these people never ventured over to the Broadview clinic. There were days when I would be afraid to look at the appointment book – sometimes there was only one patient listed.

I got married in 1980. With the money I made at my clinic and the money my wife made working as a waitress, as well as loans from relatives, we were able to put a $30,000 downpayment on the property where I had my clinic; it was listed at $163,000. Soon afterwards, Toronto experienced a big real estate boom. Three months after we made the downpayment, I was offered $300,000 for the property! I said no at the time because it seemed to me that the dreams I had for this clinic were worth more than the money. Later, though, I did move my clinic twice. Through word of mouth, I built up my practice, although the first five years were difficult. Many days there were only two or three appointments in the book; but luckily, during that whole time, there was only one day when I had no patients at all.

When I left Japan, I had a dream of becoming a successful shiatsu practitioner. My goals were quite materialistic: I dreamed of owning my own house and a big North American car. I dreamed of giving shiatsu treatments to major league baseball players, Hollywood stars, presidents of big companies and Olympic athletes. That was the kind of practice I envisioned for myself. It was a "someday" kind of dream. One of the things I had packed from home was a barbecue-style grill for making Japanese yakitori. I had figured that if I could not make my living through shiatsu, I could always be a street vendor in Niagara Falls, selling yakitori to tourists. I never had to use my little grill. In fact, all those dreams I brought with me came true during my early days in Canada. But the really wonderful thing is that being able to help people through shiatsu became much more satisfying and important to me than any of the material trappings of success. Nothing can match the satisfaction of knowing that thousands of people have had their pain eased, their health improved and their energy and creativity enhanced through their visits to my clinic.

EVEN A MOUNTAIN RISING HIGH

INTO THE SKY HAS PATHS BY WHICH

IT CAN BE CLIMBED

大空に

そりえてたてる高嶺

あふらむの道のほとり

あまりつゝ

CHAPTER 4
EXECUTIVES, ATHLETES AND MOVIE STARS

On March 14, 1981, just after my 30th birthday, I opened my own clinic called Shiatsu Dohjoh on Broadview Avenue in Toronto. Since the early days there, I have observed many business people reap the benefits of shiatsu. It was around that time that I had a call from a Japanese businessman, the Canadian president of a Japanese trading company. It was the 25th anniversary of his company, and he had arranged to host a huge anniversary bash at his Bayview Avenue mansion. When the time came, he was struck with back pain so severe that he was worried he would not be able to stand up straight and properly host the party. I agreed to do a home visit. The treatment brought him great relief, and he was so pleased with the results that he introduced me to the Canadian president of a Japanese automobile corporation. This gentleman was also interested in having treatments, so I made a couple of house calls for him. One day, he asked me about the difference between chiropractic and shiatsu therapy. I explained that chiropractic is an American therapy started in the United States, whereas shiatsu is a Japanese therapy. I asked him, "Which is better: a Japanese car or an American car?" He laughed.

By the early 1980s, the Western world was beginning to recognize the quality behind the words Made in Japan. All things Japanese, from automobiles and electronics to karate and sushi, started to take off. The timing was good for me to begin introducing high-quality "made in Japan" shiatsu. Japanese manufacturers started opening factories throughout North America, and Japanese financial institutions were expanding abroad. Their top executives came to Toronto frequently, and I had the opportunity to meet many of them and give them shiatsu treatments. I was starting to feel that I was finally on the right course in my life.

Around that time, I was inspired to change my name from Ken-ichi to Ken-sen. Ken means "health," and ichi means "premier." I was given the name Kenichi when I was born because it was my parents' wish that I grow up making health a priority. Sen comes from the character for "fountain"; therefore Kensen means "the fountain of health." From that time on, I wanted to be the fountain of health to others.

Business and stress management

Repeatedly in my practice, I have seen shiatsu revitalize the intellectual performance of business people. Our body should harmonize with the rhythms of nature, but the rhythm of business and the rhythm of the city are crisis rhythms. A shiatsu treatment can normalize an imbalanced inner rhythm. Business people are prone to high stresses in the course of their normal workday. Shiatsu can balance the nervous system, both calming and energizing a stressed-out person. It leaves you in a relaxed state, and that state of relaxation is the key to creativity. People under great stress lose their creative edge. Shiatsu helps to restore it.

One day, I was called to the Four Seasons Hotel to give a shiatsu treatment to a promising young Japanese businessman who was visiting Toronto briefly. His computer company was being widely touted as the next Sony-type success story. Its shares were not on the open market, but if they had been they would have been very highly priced. When I started shiatsu on him, I found his back and neck to be really stiff. He was only two or three years older than I was, in his mid-30s. His body really needed that shiatsu treatment! I told him that it was important that he arrange to have regular, frequent shiatsu treatments for a while when he got home to Tokyo, but he said he was much too busy for such a thing.

Some time later, I had the opportunity to treat the new president of a Japanese car company. During his first treatment, I didn't discover anything particularly wrong but I noticed that his breathing was short and shallow. I suggested that he try long, deep breaths, especially exhaling slowly, and I gave him some breathing exercises to practise regularly. As a health care practitioner, I try to give suggestions to all of my patients to help them improve their health, whether it's teaching simple stretching exercises, recommending they stop smoking or talking about a healthy diet. The next time they visit, I ask, "Did you take my advice?" Very few have, perhaps one in 20. Most people look for quick fix but don't put any effort into disciplining themselves. When I gave my second treatment to the car company president, I found to my surprise that his condition was much improved. His abdomen felt much softer and better. When I commented on this, his wife spoke up. She told me that he had followed my advice to do breathing exercises whenever he had a spare minute in his very busy schedule. I was very impressed that he had taken this advice so seriously and that I could observe such a physical improvement by the second treatment. I was in my early 30s and unknown at the time, and he was in his 50s and in a very important position. It was clear to me that he was the kind of person who, upon hearing good advice, listened to it and acted on it, even if it came from someone younger. I couldn't help but feel that was one of the traits that made him so effective in his senior position.

About a month after I treated this executive, a university friend of mine, a chartered accountant from Tokyo, visited me and we went out for a drink and a chat. I told him that he should advise all his clients to buy that Japanese car company's stock. He was surprised to hear me say that because all the reports in the business press were down on that company. But I felt strongly that after doing shiatsu on any executive, I could reliably predict not only the person's own health but could quite confidently predict the health of his company as well. By contrast, I did not recommend investing in the computer company of the young businessman who had ignored my advice. Two years later, during a visit to Tokyo, I met with my friend and he said that what I had predicted that day in Toronto had, in fact, come true: the young businessman's computer company had to sell out, but the car company's sales had soared. The body tells many things, I thought to myself. I am certainly not a fortune teller, but sometimes the practice of shiatsu gives me insight into what is likely to happen.

Managers have a lot of decisions to make, and they need a kind of intuition, calling on their past experiences to do so. Making these decisions in unhealthy conditions can cause things to turn out badly. That is why I believe a manager's own health is an essential factor. People in a state of exhaustion cannot make proper judgements. When I treat business people, I often pay attention to the neck and the abdomen, because stiffness in the neck will prevent them from doing business well. Achieving a soft neck through regular shiatsu is important; likewise, a soft abdomen has positive effects on personality.

Playing in the major league

In the spring of 1986, a talented major league baseball player came to my clinic. I had no idea who he was at first. He filled out the usual patient record form, and under occupation he wrote baseball pitcher. I asked him questions about his physical condition, and he explained to me that he had strained his thigh at spring training camp and was having elbow trouble. It happened to be the opening day of the season, but he was not at the stadium because he was on the disabled list. I started the treatment, and he complained of pain in his elbow, but I soon found that the real problem was in his neck. It was very stiff, and it would take a long time to correct it. As I treated him, it became clear he had splendid muscles. Although I had worked on many patients who kept themselves fit, I had never before touched so many well-developed muscles. I said, "You must be good at your job." Then he told me he had been the second-best save pitcher in the league two years earlier, which was impressive indeed. When I finished the treatment, I advised him to come back. My next patient was an American businessman, and I asked him if he had heard of the baseball player Bill Caudill. The man spent his whole treatment telling me how great and well respected Caudill was. I learned that Caudill was the first million-dollar player ever signed by the Toronto Blue Jays. It then dawned on me that for many years I had been so intent on my work seven days a week that I had no time to keep up with things like baseball and movies. Clients were coming through the door who were well known to everyone but me!

A couple of days later, Bill came back for his second treatment and he said he felt much better. But I found his neck was still in bad shape, and I could tell as I worked on it that if he did not have frequent, regular treatments to fix it, he was going to be in big trouble before long. I always tried to be positive with all of my patients, so I told Bill that I felt if he came for shiatsu regularly he could enjoy a long career in baseball. Looking back, I wish I had told him the flip side of that, which I was aware of at the time but did not want to say because it sounded so negative. I should have said, "If you don't get this problem in your neck treated regularly, your baseball career will be over soon." Bill had a few shiatsu treatments and felt he was much improved. Then he went back to playing and immediately made his first save of the season. He did not come back for shiatsu to treat the underlying problem in his neck, though. I followed his career through television and the newspapers for a while. Every time he was sent to the mound, the team was already in a tense situation, so any mistake he made would cost the team and thousands of fans would judge him harshly. It seemed a terrible position for him to be in when he had the underlying physical problem. He went into each situation with his neck already stressed, and he immediately faced an enormous amount of pressure, with every eye focused on him. He did not do very well that season, and at the end of it he had to hang up his peaked cap for good. I felt frustrated as I watched and found myself wishing I had told him more directly that the neck problem had to be addressed immediately and at length or the consequences would be dire. I also felt frustrated when I saw the newspaper reports claiming that the team had paid too much for him. It was not true. The truth was Bill did have a million-dollar body. He could have played much better if the problem in his neck had been cleared up.

I learned a lot from that experience. Ever since, I have made sure I'm straightforward with patients, even if the news is not easy for them to hear. Working with Bill was also my first experience doing shiatsu on a million-dollar body, and my thumbs had come to appreciate the kind of muscle development a person can achieve. In the case of both professional and amateur athletes, men and women, the best players have topnotch bone structures, joints, muscles and tendons for their specific sport. Their abilities are partly due to the attributes they're born with but also how their body develops through training. I remember treating a female figure skater in the fall of 1979. She had accidentally run into her partner during practice, causing a terrible whiplash-type injury. After treating her neck and proceeding to treat the rest of her body, I was shocked to discover the thickness of her Achilles tendon: it was two, maybe three, times thicker than normal. I asked more about her and learned she was Canadian figure skating champion Lorna Wighton, who had been selected to go to the Winter Olympics in Lake Placid. My thumbs were stunned as I committed to memory the Achilles tendon of a champion ice skater.

Following a million dollars with gold

In the spring of 1986, I had been practising shiatsu for about five years at Shiatsu Dohjoh on Broadview Avenue. One day, a young rhythmic gymnast who lived in our neighbourhood and who came to me regularly for treatments called me from the gym where she trained and explained that the 1984 Olympic gold medallist in rhythmic gymnastics, Lori Fung, had just arrived from Vancouver with a very sore foot. My client asked if she could send Lori to my clinic. When Lori arrived, she was worried that she might have a stress fracture in her foot, a disastrous state of affairs for someone in her sport. I started her treatment and could tell right away that it was not a fracture, which was a relief to her. She found shiatsu very effective in dealing with her pain and continued to come for treatments to cope with the tension that had accumulated during two years of competing in the public eye after winning the gold medal. Her whole body exuded stress and tension that first appointment, but during the second treatment her muscles were soft and firm. I wasn't surprised; I had learned that the bodies of first-class athletes have an overwhelming ability to respond quickly.

Word begins to spread

Lori Fung was so happy with the way shiatsu helped her deal with her foot pain and reduce her stress level that she talked about it with her fellow rhythmic gymnasts. In those days, word of mouth was how most people ended up hearing about Shiatsu Dohjoh. I was no longer just waiting for people to come to me; they started to seek me out. A cosmetics company, the third largest in the world, asked me to help promote its overseas product line, called Essential Energy Body Care Products. When the company's more than 200 beauty consultants met for a convention, I was asked to present a seminar on easy-to-do hand and facial shiatsu, accompanied by a brief lecture. On another occasion, a special stage was erected at the Toronto Eaton Centre so that I could give shiatsu demonstrations. For customers who bought the line of products, I performed a 15-minute shiatsu treatment in a chair.

One day, I got a phone call from a woman who told me that she was the

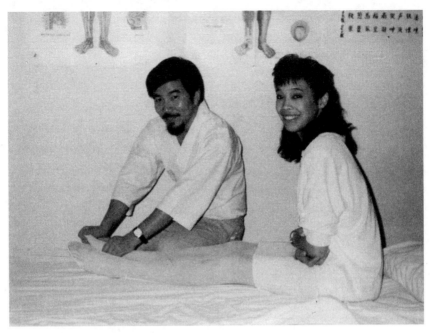

Treating Olympic gold medallist Lori Fung, 1986.

manager for a film star. The actor was shooting a movie in Toronto and wondered if I was available to give him a treatment. I agreed and went on a house call to an address on Bayview Avenue. When I arrived, I saw two young men playing soccer on the front lawn. As I got out of my car, one of them came over and introduced himself. Little did I know he was a famous Hollywood star. He invited me to come inside and, as I started the treatment, he told me he had just finished shooting a film. As we talked, he explained he was from Australia and had visited Japan. During the treatment, I asked him, "Do you have a problem with your gums or teeth around the back of your mouth?" He was surprised and wanted to know how I knew without looking inside his mouth. I told him there was one spot in his shoulder that indicated a problem; that particular spot often reflects trouble with the wisdom teeth. He said that it was true – he had trouble with a wisdom tooth on that side.

The following day, I was working with one of my regular patients, a woman from Australia. She is a freelance writer who happens to be a big fan of that particular movie star. I started telling her about him, and because of her interest she wrote an article for The Toronto Star about the therapeutic value of shiatsu, mentioning that I had treated a big-name star while he was in Toronto for a film shoot. The paper ran a photograph of me treating one of my regular clients, a woman who suffers from Crohn's disease. The caption and the article drew a lot of interest. Not long after, I started noticing a significant increase in the number of young women booking appointments. Wondering why, I asked my staff and some of my patients. It turns out they were calling and saying, "I want to be treated by the hands that touched my favourite movie star!" The little clinic that I had begun when I was 30 was now well on its way to success after five years.

Shiatsu therapy relieves stress

Rock stars, athletes and actors among clients seeking massage

By Susan Martin
Special to The Star

When the president of the Toyota Motor Co. comes to Canada, one of his first stops is Toronto. Here, at the hands of shiatsu therapist Ken Saito, the busy Japanese executive finds relief from the tensions of a hectic day.

Few people know stress, the modern malaise, better than "Kensen," the Tokyo-trained shiatsu therapist who's treated everyone from athletes to rock stars in his Broadview Ave. clinic. Olympic gold medalist Lori Fung, TV personality Ann Rohmer and actor Mel Gibson have been there for therapy.

Stresses and strains are a way of life for many, but stress spells a loss of "essential energy," that can result in illness and fatigue, Saito says.

"Essential energy is the basis of Oriental philosophy," adds Saito, 35, who came to Toronto nearly seven years ago.

Essential energy

"People often remark that people in the Orient look younger than Western people. That's because in the Orient they incorporate the concept of essential energy into their lifestyle." The Japanese, he says, visit shiatsu therapists several times a month.

But when the body is naturally relaxed there's a continuous flow of energy, he says. Stress causes the energy to stop or back up, which manifests itself in physical wear and tear. Using the thumb, fingers and palms of the hand to manipulate certain pressure points, or "tsubos," liberates the flow of energy, Saito says.

Shiatsu massage, or pressure-point therapy, originated in China 5,000 years ago as a treatment for both physical and emotional disorders. It was adopted by the Japanese about 4,000 years later as an

occupation for the blind. Today in Japan, shiatsu is a recognized form of alternative medicine and all shiatsu practitioners are licensed.

Introduced in Canada and almost exclusively to Ontario 15 years ago, shiatsu is not regulated here. Some provinces, like British Columbia, have no shiatsu practitioners at all.

Shiatsu's appeal seems to come from its holistic approach. There is more to the art than mere physical manipulation. The esthetic value of touch therapy plays an important role.

The therapist takes the whole individual into account, discussing lifestyle, diet and exercise, says Alf Walker, a Toronto therapist.

Gaining popularity

This way of thinking has even caught on in the corporate world.

Last year, the third largest cosmetic company in the world, Shiseido (America) Ltd., introduced its Essential Energy body-care products incorporating the tenets of shiatsu massage in its marketing strategy.

They enlisted Saito's expertise in the training of more than 200 Shiseido beauty consultants. Customers buying Shiseido products are shown the basic pressure points in the store, and provided with how-to brochures that accompany their moisturizing and cleansing creams.

Although the Shiatsu Therapy Association of Ontario imposes its own standards, membership in the association requires at least 2,200 hours of formal training in shiatsu massage, the same number of hours as a registered massage therapist. In addition, students must study anatomy, physiology and pathology.

According to association president Walker, there are "hundreds" of lay practitioners using shiatsu massage on their family and friends, but there's also a "hand-

ful" who purport to be professionals, but who aren't. The 51 members of the association, the majority of whom are in Metro Toronto, are attempting to set professional standards to keep the unqualified people out. All members are graduates of accredited courses recog-

nized by either the Nippon Shiatsu Association of Japan or approved by the provincial Ministry of Colleges and Universities, private vocational schools branch. (A list of qualified practitioners is available from the association by calling 762-2260.)

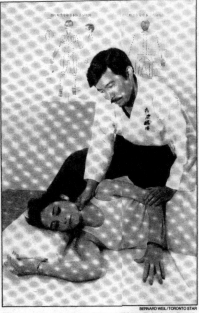

Pressure-point therapy: Ken Saito, of Shiatsu Dohjoh on Broadview Ave., applies his skills as a shiatsu therapist on Jennifer Neufeld, who suffers from Crohn's disease, a bowel disorder.

BERNARD WEIL/TORONTO STAR

This 1986 Toronto Star article sparked a lot of interest in shiatsu. The photo shows me treating a patient who suffers from Crohn's disease.

WALKING ON A STEEP MOUNTAIN PATH

REMINDS ONE OF THE DIFFICULTIES

THAT PEOPLE WENT THROUGH TO MAKE

THE PATH LONG AGO

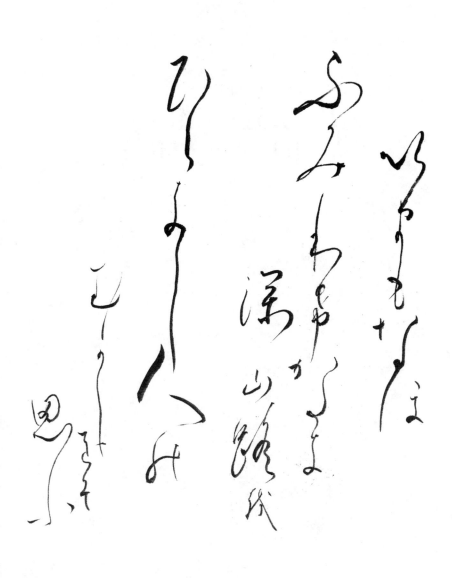

CHAPTER 5
THE GREAT MENTOR IN MY LIFE

Toru Namikoshi (left) and Tokujiro Namikoshi (right) with B.J. Palmer, principal of the Palmer College of Chiropractic in Iowa, 1953.

To have a friend we can share our dreams with is indeed special, and for me that close friend was Toru Namikoshi, the eldest son of my teacher, Tokujiro Namikoshi. When I dreamed of opening a shiatsu school in connection with my Toronto clinic, Toru encouraged me, helped me and provided a lot of documentation to support my application to the government. When Toru dreamed of organizing a big international shiatsu conference in Toronto, I vowed I would help make it happen. Although he was 20 years older, we shared many similar beliefs and attitudes. We dedicated ourselves to the same profession and became very close over the years.

Shiatsu goes abroad

Toru was born on the island of Hokkaido in 1931. Growing up, he was always very interested in the arts; when it was time for him to go to university, he opted to study fine arts at Nihon University. When he was a young man, the first Pacific mayors conference was held in Tokyo in 1952, and his father offered to give shiatsu therapy to the delegates attending from the United States. Toru worked alongside his father for this event. Some of the mayors were deeply impressed by the experience, and Toru's life took a curious turn soon afterwards. When the mayor of an Iowa city who had attended the conference returned home, he got in touch with B.J. Palmer, the head of a local chiropractic college, to tell him about shiatsu and about Tokujiro Namikoshi. Palmer, the son of the founding father of chiropractic, was so intrigued that he invited both Tokujiro and Toru to lead a workshop at the college in 1953. They accepted his invitation. It was the first time that shiatsu made its way to North America.

When the demonstration in Iowa was over, Tokujiro flew back to Tokyo, but Toru stayed in Iowa to pursue studies at the chiropractic college as an exchange student. He ended up staying in the United States for seven years. At the outset, he experienced many social difficulties at the college. It had been only eight years since the end of the Second World War, and many of his classmates were former GIs. As a Japanese man, Toru was widely resented. But he persisted and, in time, built up a network of friends.

One day, Toru went for a drive with two friends. They were in a terrible accident, which killed his companions instantly. Toru was thrown from the car and lost consciousness. He was eventually found and taken to the hospital, but he did not receive prompt or extensive attention there, and later he couldn't help but think that stemmed from lingering anti-Japanese sentiments. He was left with terrible headaches, nausea, weakness in his arms and a variety of whiplash symptoms. He practised shiatsu on his head and body to try to overcome the problems. Throughout his career, he always emphasized the benefits of self-administered shiatsu.

The Hollywood connection

While Toru was in Iowa, a friend of his father's arrived one day to deliver to Toru some American money that Marilyn Monroe had given Tokujiro after a shiatsu treatment during her Tokyo honeymoon in 1956. This friend was an actor himself, a star of the silent screen: Sessue Hayakawa. Sessue was the first Japanese actor to become an international star in silent films. Sessue's show business career languished after talking films became popular, and he lived in Paris throughout the Second World War. After the war, he was called back to Hollywood to make the film Tokyo Joe with Humphrey Bogart. Bogart identified with him because both men had especially large faces; Bogart was self-conscious about his.

Sessue met Tokujiro Namikoshi when he had knee trouble and went to him for shiatsu to clear it up. The two men became fast friends. Sessue was cast as the general in the hit film The Bridge over the River Kwai (1957), which was filmed in Thailand. When he came to Iowa to give Toru Marilyn Monroe's money, all of Toru's classmates recognized him from the movies, so Toru learned that his father's friend was a star in the United States. When Toru eventually moved to Los Angeles, he visited Sessue. He was surprised when Sessue said to Toru and the entourage present, "Let's go for a drink" – his experience in those days in the United States was that many restaurants had Japanese Not Welcome signs on their front doors. Was there really a place Japanese were allowed in for a drink? he wondered. Sessue took them all to a nightclub. As soon as they arrived, the club manager had a word with the orchestra leader, who stopped the dance number they were playing and launched into the theme from The Bridge over the River Kwai. Sessue and his entourage started to march around the dance floor, then Toru decided to join in, and they all marched to their table in time with the music.

In contrast to his father's sparkling, outgoing manner, it was Toru's nature to be quiet, careful and steady. When he returned to Japan from his studies in the United States, he became assistant director of the Japan Shiatsu School and went on to hone his skills as a master practitioner in Tokyo and win great respect for his work.

Every spring, Toru and his students did free open-air shiatsu for the public in Tokyo-Ueno Park. He wrote about shiatsu in both Japanese and English, made yearly trips to Canada, the United States and Europe to lead seminars, and advised shiatsu practitioners everywhere he went.

My teacher, Tokujiro, organized the first international shiatsu conference in Tokyo in 1979 in order to spread knowledge about shiatsu and cultivate international friendships. Like most Japanese people, Tokujiro never wanted the world to experience the horror of another nuclear bomb like the ones dropped in 1945 on Hiroshima and Nagasaki. He longed for nations to stop fighting and believed that the principles of caring and giving that embody the art of shiatsu could nurture harmony and understanding among people, and thereby promote world peace. The second, third and fourth conferences were held in Rome/Amsterdam, Honolulu and Taipei, respectively. In 1986, Vancouver hosted the fifth international shiatsu conference. More than 500 people lined up for shiatsu demonstrations, sitting on chairs at the Japanese pavilion on the grounds of Expo.

An assistant with incredible luck

While at the conference, I told Toru how my shiatsu practice was beginning to get very busy and I was thinking of getting an assistant. I asked if he could recommend a graduate of his school. His answer quite overwhelmed me: "How about my son?" he proposed. I did not know what to say, feeling honoured but also a little hesitant about accepting such a responsibility. He was keen that his son Takashi have the experience of working at my clinic, and I was thrilled. In January of the following year, Takashi arrived with another graduate of the school, both of them eager to help and to learn.

One day shortly after their arrival, I took Takashi to the corner grocery store on an errand. In those days, Japan didn't yet have scratch-and-win lottery tickets, and he was very curious about them when he spotted them in the store. Each day thereafter, whenever he had disappeared and I would ask where he was, my staff would say he had gone to the corner to buy another scratch game card. I was appalled. I had introduced the son of my respected mentor to gambling. One Saturday, I took Takashi aside and told him that this had to stop. I told him firmly that I myself had never won a scratch-and-win lottery in eight years, that it was a complete waste of time and money. He was only 24 years old and did not have extra money to throw away. I asked him to stop buying the cards, and he agreed. Later that evening when I got home, the phone rang. It was Takashi, and he was excited. "Mr. Saito, I just won $10,000 on a scratch-and-win card," he exclaimed. I went over to meet him and, sure enough*, he had a $10,000 winning card. We went for a drink to celebrate his win, and on the way he darted into another variety store and bought another two tickets before I could stop him. He won another $100! The store owner was surprised because he had never before sold a $100 winning ticket. And when Takashi pulled out the $10,000 winning ticket, the store owner almost fell over. But no one was more astonished than I was.

That summer, I invited Takashi's mother, Matsuko Namikoshi, for a visit to see how her son was getting along. I took the two of them to dinner at Benihana restaurant in the Royal York Hotel. As we sat at the hibachi table, Matsuko asked me to tell her the story of how I had come to live in Canada. I told her everything and explained that I had originally been inspired by the story of Rocky Aoki, who, with very little money, moved from Japan to New York in search of success and after much hard work eventually made his fortune as the founder of the successful chain of Benihana restaurants, including the one we were sitting in. For my generation, he was an inspiration, the embodiment of the "American dream." As I was telling my story, Takashi interrupted me. "Mr. Saito," he said insistently. "There's Rocky Aoki!" We glanced over at the table he was indicating and, sure enough, there was Rocky Aoki, so we went over to say hello. I asked if he came to Toronto often. It was the first time in 15 years, he said. Luck just seemed to follow Takashi wherever he went. He stayed in Canada for a year and enjoyed both his Canadian shiatsu experiences and his lottery experiences.

Toru and I spent time together whenever he came to Toronto, when I made

Takashi Namikoshi, Rocky Aoki (founder of the Benihana restaurant chain) and I at Benihana, Royal York Hotel, Toronto, 1987.

trips back to Tokyo or when we met elsewhere for shiatsu events. In 1990, which was the 50th anniversary of the opening of Japan Shiatsu College (the name had changed from Japan Shiatsu School to Japan Shiatsu College in 1981), Tokujiro turned over the directorship of the college to Toru as a token of respect for his eldest son's abilities. Part of Toru's job was to keep abreast of the international shiatsu community, and at about that time he noticed that the word shiatsu had been included in the Oxford English Dictionary, the definition being "a kind of therapy, of Japanese origin, in which pressure is applied with the thumbs and palms to certain points on the body." Its inclusion in the dictionary meant it was now in common usage in the English language. Toru recalled a time during the 1950s when he had asked his father if it might be better to use the phrase "finger pressure therapy" among North Americans instead of the word shiatsu so that they could instantly grasp what it entailed. But Tokujiro

THE GREAT MENTOR IN MY LIFE

had disagreed, saying that judo had become a universally recognized term; shiatsu would too. So, nearly 40 years after father and son first introduced shiatsu outside of Japan, the word itself had been adopted as they had hoped.

Seeking approval to establish a school

The same year, I applied to the Ontario government for a permit to open a school of shiatsu. The next four years brought many frustrations as I sought approval from the provincial education ministry, but Toru stood by me and gave me his encouragement and help the whole time. When I flew to Tokyo in 1992 to celebrate Tokujiro's 88th birthday with his family and friends, as well as to attend the 10th international shiatsu conference, I got a pleasant surprise. I received a message from Dennis Mills, my federal Member of Parliament and one of my regular patients. In his fax, he pledged that he would do all he could to ensure that someday shiatsu would be integrated into the nation's health care system. I read his message aloud to the 1,000 people attending the conference, and the following day I took it to the Canadian embassy in Tokyo. By sheer coincidence, the official who came to talk with me about it was the same man who had interviewed me 12 years earlier when I wanted to move to Canada. He remembered me and recalled telling me there was no need for shiatsu practitioners in Canada. This positive message from Ottawa impressed him greatly, and he said he was happy that he had approved me as an immigrant and was pleased to learn that I was making a contribution in Canada. I returned to Toronto in a very positive frame of mind. A few weeks later, I received a parcel from Tokyo: it was a Doctor of Shiatsu degree from the Japan Shiatsu Association.

By now, I was teaching shiatsu to several students in my Toronto Shiatsu Academy, including two referred to me by the Ontario Ministry of Labour. One day, I got a call from an official with the education ministry, demanding that I close my school immediately. I found this very strange. I had just received the official message from Ottawa, and an Ontario ministry was referring students to me, but the education officials wanted to close me down. I consulted a lawyer and eventually the officials

Tokujiro (left), Toru (right) and I at the Hotel New Ohtani in Tokyo, 1990, celebrating the opening of the Toronto Shiatsu Academy.

backed off. I sometimes felt frustrated dealing with the Ontario education ministry on the approval process. Four years had gone by since I had applied and I still had no word.

My first class consisted of 14 students, with Canadians and immigrants from places as diverse as Hong Kong, Japan, Aruba, El Salvador, Guyana and Czechoslovakia. It has always pleased me very much that my students come from so many different corners of the world. During that first year, I taught them each shiatsu, and my associate, Dr. George Chiu, taught anatomy, physiology and pathology. I had met Dr. Chiu on a flight from Tokyo to Toronto. Formerly a surgeon in Taiwan, he had decided to retire in Toronto and develop his interest in holistic medicine. He had heard of shiatsu but was not clear on exactly what it was or how it worked. During the flight, I told him my story, outlined my plans to set up a school and asked if he would help. I felt his experience and knowledge would be a great asset: he had studied medicine in Japan and worked as a military physician in Vietnam, then became chief surgeon in a Taipei hospital, where he practised for 25 years. He had come to feel uneasy about trying to solve all medical problems through surgery and medications, so he had decided to leave his job and study a broader approach to health.

I had no idea how I could pay Dr. Chiu's teaching salary, but we struck a deal. His wife suffered terribly from lower back pain, so while he taught my students evening classes, I gave shiatsu treatments to his wife. Doctors had told her she needed an operation on her back, but she and her husband weren't comfortable with that. After three years of shiatsu treatments, a medical specialist friend of theirs in Boston showed them comparative X-rays of her back, taken before and after the shiatsu. The earlier X-ray showed the nerve's canal compressed on the nerve. After three years of shiatsu, the canal had visibly widened. She was not surprised since her pain was largely relieved.

Four years later, David Sugarman, who works at the Ontario Science Centre, came to teach with us, adding to the shiatsu program's scientific foundation. As well, Toru Namikoshi gave me both moral support and practical help during that time, and I felt very grateful to know he cared.

In the spring of 1993, I travelled to the Netherlands, where Denis Binks was opening the European Shiatsu Academy. Toru and Takashi were there with two others from their organization, and afterwards we travelled together to England; while there, we took in a performance of Kiss of the Spider Woman, starring Canadian Brent Carver. In the fall of that year, I went to Melbourne, Australia, to attend the 11th international shiatsu conference. Afterwards, Toru and I went on to Sydney to lecture on women's health and give shiatsu demonstrations. In Australia at that time, medications were being widely used to manage menopause, and many women suffered side effects. Australian health care practitioners were seeking a more holistic approach to these menopausal problems.

Saying goodbye to a dear friend

On May 18, 1994, the phone rang after my evening class. It was Takashi Namikoshi; he said his father was dying. Toru was only 63. We'd been planning to go to Peru together that August to give a shiatsu seminar. My mind went blank as I heard Takashi's words: Toru had had two operations and was now on life support. He had suffered a subarachnoid haemorrhage in his brain and was left brain dead. There was no hope.

I could not sleep all night. I tried to get a plane ticket for the next morning, yet at the same time I felt compelled to do what Toru would have wanted me to do: honour my commitments to my scheduled patients and students first. I worked that day and booked my flight for the following day. That afternoon, as I tried my best to carry on through my sorrow about Toru, an official from the education ministry appeared to tell me that my application had finally been approved and asked me to come to their offices the next morning to sign the appropriate papers. I explained to him that a dear friend who had also been waiting for this approval for four years was dying in Tokyo and that my plane left at 10 in the morning. He agreed that my lawyer could sign the papers in my place.

I could not stop the flow of tears all the way to Tokyo. I wanted to tell Toru that we had finally been granted approval for the school, and I brought along the new school brochure to show him. As soon as I got to Tokyo, I rushed to the hospital. Just as I arrived, they were disconnecting the life support equipment. Still, I got to tell him that the school he had helped plan had been approved. I have always sensed that the education official's timing was some final push of Toru's willpower. Otherwise, I simply cannot explain how it happened at exactly that moment, after we had been waiting for four years.

Toru died on May 20, 1994. I stayed in Tokyo for two weeks after his death. During that time, I reflected often on one of the great dreams we shared: that someday there would be an international shiatsu meeting in Toronto. So at the funeral, I promised that we would hold the very next international conference in Toronto and

THE GREAT MENTOR IN MY LIFE

we would dedicate it to Toru's memory. I also kept thinking about the automobile accident he had had in his 20s in Iowa; I've always believed that the accident and lack of proper care afterwards were contributing factors in his early death. The kind of haemorrhage he had can be linked to previous brain damage. Undoubtedly there was also a genetic factor; his mother had died at 54 of a brain haemorrhage. About his son, Tokujiro said that perhaps it was his destiny that having done excellent work he could pass away early. At the funeral, he recited a poem he had written. I will always remember this line: "To master the shiatsu-doh, Toru gave his life to his father."

Moving forward in Toru's memory

After Toru's death, Tokujiro resumed the job of principal of the Japan Shiatsu College, no easy task for an 89-year-old man. He vowed to dedicate his remaining days to his son's work. That was the only way he could cope with Toru's death. I felt great compassion for Tokujiro. He had lost two wives and now his beloved son. Losing your child is devastating at any age, but on top of that, Toru had been Tokujiro's successor in his life's work. It was a terrible loss for him, as it was for me. Not only had Toru been my mentor but also a close friend, like a soulmate. We had worked towards the same goals and were very close. To honour Toru in my heart, I knew I needed to ensure the success of both an international conference in Toronto dedicated to him and the school he had helped me realize. So upon returning to Toronto, I initiated plans for the conference. The following year, in July 1995, more than 400 shiatsu practitioners and friends from Italy, Spain, the Netherlands, Japan, Canada, Mexico, France, Taiwan, the United States and other countries took part in the 12th international shiatsu conference in Toronto, honouring Toru Namikoshi. On opening night, we were delighted to have Tony Award winner Brent Carver sing "Sukiyaki" in Japanese; he spent a lot of time practising it. Lenore Zann donned a Marilyn Monroe costume and sang theme songs from Monroe's films, dedicating them to Tokujiro, who was then 90. Delegates still talk about their terrific memories of that conference. On the afternoon of the second day, practitioners from around the world took part in

Brent Carver, Tokujiro, Lenore Zann and I at the 12th international shiatsu congress in Toronto, 1995. Brent and Lenore performed for the delegates.

Open-Air Shiatsu at Ontario Place, a tribute to the promotional open-air shiatsu-on-a-chair events first introduced by Toru in Tokyo-Ueno Park about 20 years earlier.

My commitment to develop the Toronto school was also very important to me. If I continued to give treatments only, perhaps seven or eight people a day could benefit, but if I trained others, the benefits would reach many more. I had started to do some training in 1990, but when I got permission from the Ontario education ministry to run a government-approved school, I expanded the curriculum in 1994. Still, at the time, shiatsu had no municipal classification in Toronto; it fell under the category "body rub parlour," which meant there were zoning restrictions regarding where it could be practised. Labelling shiatsu as a body rub service is an example of how preventive health care has been seriously undervalued in our country. In contrast, shiatsu has been recognized by the Ministry of Health in Japan since 1955. In 1997, the

THE GREAT MENTOR IN MY LIFE

European Economic Community added shiatsu to the list of non-conventional therapies, alongside chiropractic, acupuncture and osteopathy. After much lobbying by Toronto shiatsu professionals, particularly the Shiatsu Diffusion Society, Metro By-Law 20-84 was established in 1997, allowing shiatsu to be practised under the Holistic Practitioners Licence. We were then able to offer the first class of our full-time two-year program that fall.

In October 2002, I decided to change my clinic name from Shiatsu Dohjoh to Shiatsu Masters, and I opened a second clinic right in the heart of the business district in downtown Toronto. There, we offer treatments ranging from 20 to 50 minutes. I knew shorter sessions would be a welcome service since business people were pressed for time; I had already had occasion to treat people right at their workplaces. One time, a downtown computer company hired me to give 20-minute sessions to each executive and company officer once a week over a three-month period. When TSN, the sports television network, celebrated its 10th anniversary several years ago, it formed a personal care troupe, which included me as the shiatsu practitioner. Over a four-week period, the troupe was sent to the network's major area clients, about 40 advertising agencies in and around Toronto. People in advertising were in real need of shiatsu, I found. They were always up against crucial deadlines and were constantly pressured. I could tell from their bodies that they were carrying a lot of stress. What they really needed was regular and complete shiatsu treatments in a calm and quiet environment, but all we had was 20 minutes in the midst of the turmoil. Still, that 20 minutes of shiatsu really helped to release tension, even in less than ideal settings. Patients told us that they were more relaxed and focused on their work after a shiatsu treatment. I am convinced that shiatsu could go a long way towards easing the friction in all those financial towers and increasing productivity noticeably, a benefit to both employee and employer.

HEALTH AND TRUST
ARE THE
HIGHEST PRIZES

健康と信用
最高の宝也

CHAPTER 6
THE BENEFITS OF SHIATSU: PATIENT TESTIMONIALS

In this chapter, I share a collection of testimonials, but first I would like to explain my motive in doing so. In the testimonials, people speak very openly about their thoughts on shiatsu and experiences with it. I do not intend to boast about my own practice nor to criticize other therapies and approaches. My hope is that you will examine these testimonials to find out what others have discovered.

Since founding the Shiatsu Diffusion Society in 1989, my colleagues and I have published a series of newsletters called Thumbs Up for Shiatsu. In this chapter, I have reprinted some testimonials from those newsletters and from other publications, such as newspapers, as well as excerpts from direct interviews with patients.

As you read these letters and interviews, you'll make some very interesting discoveries. First, these testimonials demonstrate how shiatsu has had positive effects in a broad variety of cases. Second, it's fascinating to note how each of these individuals was led down a particular path to discover the benefits of the Japanese healing art. I had a similar experience before discovering shiatsu. I started off depending on non-natural medical care but eventually left my doctor and his medications to follow shiatsu. As a result, I chose a career as a shiatsu practitioner because shiatsu is based on a solid foundation of applying thumb and finger pressure, which triggers a universal healing source – natural healing power.

In general, I believe that there is a valid reason for every healing method to exist. No matter what method one practises, solid training and knowledge of human biology and how the body functions are essential. Since shiatsu has demonstrated indisputable positive effects, I feel strongly that it should be recognized by the ministries of health in this country as a healing method on par with other accepted methods. Furthermore, because public acceptance of shiatsu is now widespread and growing, it makes sense that health insurance coverage be introduced to make shiatsu more accessible.

"Patient Interview," January 1990

David Ochotta, a professional tennis coach, began teaching tennis at the age of 16. He has always enjoyed teaching and is now a full-time professional coach in the Pickering, Ontario, area. After a serious wrist injury that necessitated his switching hands to teach, David found shiatsu to be very therapeutic in speeding his recovery. He says, "Shiatsu is excellent for me because of how deep it gets into the muscles. That's what I really like. I think it makes a big difference." David has been a regular weekly client of Kensen's for the past five years. Shiatsu treatments have helped reduce his physical stress, and David has found that he actually has more energy afterwards. One day when I asked David how his treatment would help him, he said, "Yesterday, by the end of the day, I was starting to feel tired. Tomorrow, I will feel a noticeable difference, whereas even as of the last session I wouldn't have thought twice about scooting out for the widest balls."

– Pat Gorton

"Using Shiatsu for the Relief of Multiple Sclerosis," Fall 1991

Multiple sclerosis is a progressive disease of the central nervous system. The "messages" from the brain do not reach the various nerves and muscles. Modern medical science researchers have not yet found a cure. Many patients (mostly young people) become totally paralyzed in a short period of time.

I was fortunate not to have experienced any serious discomfort or disability until the age of 50. In hindsight, I remember many minor difficulties, dating back to early childhood. My parents and teachers referred to me as "lazy." As a young wife and the mother of two healthy boys, I blamed my extreme fatigue on my busy lifestyle, and my occasional loss of balance and sudden loss of bladder control on carelessness and lack of concentration. Now all my nerve endings are alive and sensitive to touch, heat, cold and pain.

About 12 years ago, I heard about shiatsu. At the time, I was decorating steadily and was very weak and tired, and had minimal balance, total loss of bladder control and a lot of spasticity in my legs. I became very downhearted in spite of the fact that I'm normally a cheerful person, known among my family and friends as an optimist who always finds the positive side of a problem. I had reached the point where I feared the future. Driving was a nerve-racking experience. I was afraid to go on the highway although I had more than 50 years of driving experience. Physiotherapy and exercise did not help. I tried shiatsu without expectations of help but figured it couldn't hurt. After a few weekly treatments, the spasticity disappeared, and my legs stopped jerking when I wanted to sleep. After 12 years of weekly treatments, I have not deteriorated any further. I see the bright side of life again and I am not afraid to drive my car. I've learned to use the appropriate "undergarments" to avoid embarrassing situations due to the absence of bladder control. I am my old cheerful self, unafraid of living. I see my neurologist every six months, and he is very pleased with my general health. He gives me the necessary "prescription" for further weekly shiatsu treatments, and I can therefore deduct the cost as a medical expense from my personal income tax. I take no medication except a daily multivitamin. I enjoy being with family and friends.

One day in July 1986, I reached for a chair in our living room, missed it and fell, breaking my left arm below the shoulder (ulnar bone). It happened so quickly and unexpectedly that I was unable to tell exactly why and how it happened. The doctors were quite concerned and did not know how the healing would progress. After six months (a normal recovery period for that type of fracture), I was using my walker again and I sure was happy to get out of the wheelchair. Two months later, I could drive myself to shiatsu again. At that time, I still suffered a lot of pain, but two shiatsu treatments later, all the pain and discomfort were gone. My arm was back to its old self again. From this short summary, you can see why I am convinced that shiatsu is extremely important for me. I would recommend that anybody with a disturbance of the nervous system or who has had a bone or muscle injury avail themselves of this natural healing technique. I am convinced that it enables me to live a "normal" life.

– Edith Howard

"Carpal Tunnel Syndrome," Spring 1992

For many years, I suffered from pain in my upper back and neck, as well as pain and numbness in my right hand, especially at night. I received physiotherapy at various clinics, but none of it was successful. Doctors and specialists recommended an operation on my wrist after diagnosing carpal tunnel syndrome, but I refused. For a few years, I was treated by an osteopath and was given some relief, but the symptoms endured. One day, my daughter's father-in-law told us he had just gone to Shiatsu Dohjoh for treatment for his back pain and felt much better. I decided to try the treatment, and after the first visit to Kensen Saito, principal of the Shiatsu Academy, I felt better than I had in years. I was sold! I was especially pleased that shiatsu therapy is not accompanied by any prescribed drugs since I favour natural methods. I have enjoyed shiatsu treatment for the past five years. This has released tension in my neck, improved my sleep and helped my hand tremendously. I never did have that operation.

Approximately three years ago, inflammation developed in my right thumb and palm. The thumb kept cracking loudly when I moved it, and the pain was intense when I tried to bend it. My daily drive to work became an ordeal. The doctor said that the ligament was sliding away from the joint and nothing could be done; I would end up having a stiff thumb. Because I had been very busy at my job, I had neglected my regular shiatsu treatments preceding this new problem, but when I returned to Kensen, he promised that my thumb could return to normal. He told me that the cause of all this pain was stress! After a few weekly treatments, the inflammation and pain were almost gone. A few months later, my thumb was fine, and still is today. My doctor was amazed by these results and agreed that shiatsu therapy is truly excellent. I am convinced that shiatsu is important for me. I have recommended it to many friends and co-workers, and everyone has been very satisfied. I believe in it because it is natural, it releases stress, it improves circulation and it makes me feel better all over. I believe strongly that this natural therapy can only improve one's health.

– Helen Silinsky

"Legitimize Shiatsu," Summer 1992

Nine years ago, I first became aware of shiatsu when I was out shopping. I saw the sign Shiatsu Dohjoh above a door. I had strained a muscle in my upper right arm, and the pain had caused a couple of sleepless nights. I did not take painkillers because I am against putting chemicals into my system if they are unnecessary. In Austria, where I grew up, alternative methods of therapy are more accepted. I didn't think I'd get through the weekend with this unbearable pain, so I decided to try the hands-on therapy technique known as shiatsu. In my case, it saved OHIP [Ontario Health Insurance Plan] a bundle since only one shiatsu treatment was needed. I walked into the Dohjoh and Kensen was at the front desk. After a full treatment, my pain was gone and it never came back. Plus, I walked home feeling lighter and happier. I was convinced that this was the right treatment for me compared with others. By the way, I am 83 years old now and I have treatments regularly. The government does not recognize shiatsu. Speaking from personal experience, I am certain that if the government were to recognize shiatsu as a legitimate form of alternative therapy, it would not only keep medical costs down but it would also be healthier for the individual. Over this nine-year period, it has been beneficial to my mental and physical well-being.

– Hildegard Bauer

"Shiatsu: A Holistic Alternative," Spring 1994

One morning last January, I woke up with a terrible pain in my neck. I could not find relief in any position. The doctor's advice was to stay flat on my back, alternating heat and cold applications for several days in the hope that the severe muscle spasm would relax. This strategy was not successful. My doctor had prescribed very strong muscle relaxants, anti-inflammatories and painkillers. These also had little effect. Over the next few weeks, I visited a chiropractor several times and went for four weeks of cortisone injections and nerve blocks, but without lasting results. The excruciating pain always returned and was so severe that I was unable to do my job as an elementary school vice-principal. I lost quite a bit of time at work and became most discouraged with the pain, which never left. Finally, my doctor suggested I try a treatment with Kensen Saito, a highly skilled shiatsu therapist. Even my doctor had found it beneficial. I was desperate and ready to try anything. From the first treatment (I went weekly for two months), there was some measure of relief, which increased after every visit. As well, the treatment helped me relax more fully and gave me energy to work through the pain. I have continued to receive shiatsu treatments (at least one a month) and still feel improvement and relaxation after each one. The therapy has made me more aware of my body, its stresses and its needs. Therefore, I am better able to deal with these stresses both mentally and physically. I feel invigorated and healthier after a treatment and I am indeed happy to have discovered a therapy so holistic and drug-free.

I hope the Government of Ontario will recognize the benefits of this proactive method of health care and include shiatsu therapy by a competent therapist on its list of services covered by OHIP. This would, I'm sure, save a great deal of money in the long term by reducing the need for reactive, patchwork treatment for stress-related health issues.

– Noel Macartney

"My Shiatsu Experience," Fall 1994

I've been competing in swimming for seven years. I swim for the Richmond Hill [Ontario] Aquatic Club and train twice a day. I have been receiving shiatsu treatments to try to improve my training and performances at meets. Before starting, I had headaches every day. All the doctors said that they were tension headaches and that nothing could relieve the pain. Shiatsu relieved all my headaches after the first couple of treatments. The first couple of times I came for shiatsu I didn't see any improvement in my training and meet performance but found myself very stiff and sore after them. After the third treatment, I was no longer stiff or sore but felt much more relaxed and full of energy. My training improved drastically and so did my meet performances. Just this year, I qualified for the National Standard Times. I always come to

Actor Lally Cadeau was featured in an article on shiatsu in The Toronto Star, July 4, 1995: "I feel taller, straighter and better balanced" after a treatment.

the clinic when I feel stiff or have any problems. One treatment brings relief and I am able to train well. If you have any problems, I advise you to consider shiatsu.

– Jacki Strahl

"Soothing Touch," The Toronto Star, July 4, 1995

Shiatsu is often particularly successful in relieving cases of back pain, stiff necks and shoulders, carpal tunnel syndrome, whiplash, arthritis, headache, insomnia and many sports injuries, says Kensen Saito. It can often aid in speeding recovery and rehabilitation after an illness or accident, he says. It is also helpful in reducing other effects of stress on the body and in helping concentration and focus, he adds.

"I swear by it," says Dennis Mills, Liberal MP for Broadview-Greenwood, who calls shiatsu "the all-time absolute best method of stress reduction." When things get particularly tense, he'll have a treatment every 10 days. Mills and Saito first met during an election campaign six years ago when Mills was knocking on doors seeking votes. "I was under such pressure. The CBC was giving 1,000 to 1 odds against my winning, and when I knocked on Kensen's door, he gave me a treatment," Mills recalls. "That one treatment propelled me to victory; it kept me calm for the next week and kept all my coping mechanisms going." For the past four years, Saito has been teaching a two-year course in shiatsu. For $25, clients can get a shiatsu treatment from a second-year student on clinic days. A treatment from a fully qualified practitioner at Saito's centre costs $65. Treatments last about an hour. "It's rather expensive," Hildegard Bauer notes, "but it's worth it. It works without drugs, and I don't believe in putting chemicals in my body unnecessarily."

The Japanese health ministry has officially recognized shiatsu as a valid therapy since 1955 and has applied regulations and standards for practitioners since 1964. But shiatsu has no such status or regulations in Ontario.

– Janice Dineen

"My Early Introduction to Shiatsu: Part I," September 2001

Since November 1988, I had been receiving Swedish massages from a registered massage therapist in downtown Toronto. I was open to holistic health and had been reading extensively about it. I was having Swedish massages at least twice a month for one hour each time. My feeling was that they really enhanced my sense of well-being. I was content and not really looking for any further kind of treatment.

I had read many articles about shiatsu in health magazines, so I knew something about the healing benefits, but I just hadn't been moved to experience it. In November 1991, I received a gift certificate for a half-hour treatment. The certificate pushed me to the next stage, and I booked an appointment in January and went over one afternoon for my first treatment. I figured a half-hour appointment wasn't enough to really know anything, so I booked an hour massage the following week. What I experienced during that hour was such a totally different bodily response than I had ever had with Swedish massage; within a week, I had phoned my massage therapist and terminated our treatments. When I explained why, he agreed with me and said this was what it was all about – moving on to explore other healing experiences. Swedish massage certainly loosens up your muscles and promotes better overall circulation, and for that I was thankful, but I was totally unprepared for how deeply shiatsu would go and how it would begin to hit me on levels I never dreamed possible. I started to notice things happening days, weeks and months after the treatments. One of the most immediate consequences was that I no longer needed my one-hour naps right after I got home from teaching. Somehow my energy levels held me until I went to sleep at night. This was just the beginning of a five-year relationship with a group of Chinese shiatsu therapists.

– Ross Oakes

"My Early Introduction to Shiatsu: Part 2," November 2001
Sometime during the course of receiving shiatsu from a group of Chinese therapists in Mississauga [Ontario], I happened to read an article in The Toronto Star about Kensen Saito. Kensen spoke at great length about shiatsu, his academy on the Danforth, his teacher from Japan and his vision about the body's ability to heal itself. There were also interviews with many of his clients, who spoke specifically about how shiatsu had helped them achieve an enhanced state of wellness. The article gripped me so deeply that I knew I wanted to experience a treatment with Kensen as soon as possible. So I phoned the Shiatsu Academy of Tokyo the next day and booked my first appointment. The tremendous difference between Japanese shiatsu and the kind of treatment I had been receiving from the Chinese therapists both surprised me and compelled me to question whether I wanted to continue with them any longer. You see, my Chinese massage therapists had turned around my physical health overall. On a week-to-week basis, they had enormously increased my energy levels and helped me to understand

how the vital organs in my body were connected to each another. I came to appreciate that if my lung meridian was weak, my heart meridian would reflect a similar weakness. I was told that the lungs and heart were like brother and sister; what affected one would affect the other. My therapists could tell if I had been upset during the past week by touching the meridians that reflected emotions. They could actually tell me what was going on in my body. No one had ever done this for me before. For the first time, I had an intimate sense of exactly what was happening in my body. Instead of waiting for sickness to set in, I could take an active role through shiatsu towards promoting health on a day-to-day basis. I personally came to view shiatsu as medicine in the widest sense of the word.

Having said all this, though, I have come to realize that there is a tremendous difference between Japanese and Chinese shiatsu. The Chinese therapists applied tremendously deep pressure – what you would call acupressure – with their hands and elbows. It was just like acupuncture except they were using their body instead of needles. Some days, I felt so stiff that they would literally work me over until they loosened me up. The side effect would be that certain areas of my body would be sore for days. I knew that my therapist had not "hurt" me, so I simply accepted this as the price to pay for getting the energy in my body to flow in a healthy way. Sometimes the intense pain of these treatments would literally bring tears to my eyes; I could hardly believe that in order to promote wellness in my body I would have to endure so much pain. My therapists would often say, "No pain, no gain." I believed them because their treatments had helped me. My bladder problem was reversed for the first time in 40 years, and although it was never completely eliminated, my hay fever suffering was eased. Because of these treatments, I no longer got colds, and if a bug did hit me, I could flush it out in 48 hours. But now, my Japanese shiatsu treatments had begun to persuade me that I could have the wellness without the pain. As I began to speak with Kensen during my treatments, he would describe the gentleness of his approach, likening it to a mother's love. Over a period of months with him, I discovered that I was able to hold my level of wellness without experiencing so much pain.

What I felt during the treatments and what remained with me for some time was a tremendously deep sense of well-being. Something psychological and emotional had entered this healing experience which I had not anticipated, but it overwhelmed me and was deeply appreciated. I began to realize that Kensen's way of referring to shiatsu, as a mother's love, was a reality that could be recovered bodily even when it had been lost. I was reawakened to my need to experience this on a regular basis in my life. All of this brought me to the decision to stay with Kensen. Over a period of time, I was to receive solid advice about my health, especially my allergies, which totally transformed my approach. I mentioned to Kensen that I swam every day because swimming was my favourite exercise. He asked me to stop swimming in chlorinated water because the chemicals were bad for my allergies. Things improved shortly after I stopped swimming. I wasn't happy about this but I trusted Kensen. Then he went further in helping me deal with this serious allergy: he recommended that I put a spoonful of sea salt in a bowl of warm water and basically take the solution through my nostrils to naturally cleanse my whole system.

Japanese shiatsu gave me hope that I could achieve my overall health goals. At 57, I am in the best physical shape I ever have been, I take no vitamin supplements and, for the first time in years, I have gone a whole year without taking allergy medicine. I am convinced that shiatsu needs to be covered under our provincial health plan, because in my experience, shiatsu is one of the best ways to promote preventive health care.

– Ross Oakes

"Therapy That Works," February 2002

In October 1979, I was on vacation in Hawaii, where I met a gentleman from New York who was also on vacation. He happened to mention Kensen Saito, a shiatsu therapist practising in Toronto, which is my home. From the beginning of that year, I had been experiencing a very painful stiff neck, which had progressively worsened over the year. I had a series of treatments, including chiropractic, physiotherapy, anti-inflamma-

tory pills and acupuncture. Nothing would remedy the condition. I was convinced I
had a brain tumour or something deadly. The gentleman was surprised that I had not
heard of Kensen and advised me to see him as soon as I returned to Toronto. I did so,
and in just one treatment of about one hour, Kensen took the kinks out of my neck
and rendered me free of pain for the first time in almost a year.

I have continued to have treatments with him over a period of 22 years now,
and I have sent dozens of family members and friends to him. After my car was rear-
ended one time, I experienced whiplash pain. I called Kensen, and he told me to come
immediately. My doctor had suggested a collar, but Kensen said that a collar would
cause the muscles to weaken and that when it was removed I'd be back to square one.
Kensen worked his magic, and I had no whiplash pain.

I was compelled to write this testimonial because I recently paid a visit to
Kensen following a very bad fall. The impact was very severe and I had injured my
knee so badly that my leg would not straighten and my entire body ached from the
impact. After one session, I was free of the knee pain, and when I went back for a
half-hour session, there was nothing to remind me of the fall. It is most unfortunate
that OHIP refuses to recognize the value of this therapy. They will partially pay for
chiropractic, and they pay for physiotherapy, which in my case would have taken
months to yield any results, rather than a few sessions as shiatsu did. If the medical
powers that be would take a look at the comparatively low cost of shiatsu (two treatments cost about $120) as opposed to the alternatives (which cost 10 times as much),
they would realize that our almost depleted health care funds would be better spent
on a therapy that works. The cost of shiatsu is a stretch for me financially as I am
now retired, but the benefit to my overall health is too valuable to do without.

– Margaret Stewart

"The Benefits of Shiatsu," July 2002
My introduction to shiatsu came early in 1996 when I was attending a home show in
Toronto. When I was about to leave the show, I noticed a group of soon-to-graduate

shiatsu students giving sample treatments. For most of my adult life, I had been having chiropractic treatments for migraines and backaches, with limited relief. I had read articles about shiatsu therapy, some positive and some negative – the negative explaining how some practitioners use elbows, knees and sometimes full body weight to exert pressure. The negative ones influenced me enough that I decided not to seek this type of treatment. I later found out that Namikoshi's shiatsu method uses only thumbs, fingers and palms. Standing there at the home show, feeling extremely fatigued and with my lower back aching from all the standing, I decided to take advantage of the students' offer. The session lasted about 20 minutes, at the end of which time I felt such rejuvenation it was difficult to believe the extent of relief. My back was no longer aching, my fatigue had vanished, and I was left with a pleasant feeling of relaxed fatigue and a lightness of body as though it had, to a certain extent, been released from the pull of gravity.

This experience led me to seek out a permanent therapist, whom I found in Kensen Saito. I have been having regular therapy since then, and the benefits have proven to be numerous: fewer and less severe headaches; relief of backaches and tension in the neck and shoulder area; lowering of high blood pressure; less insomnia; ability to breathe more deeply; fewer episodes of short-term memory loss that come with aging; and a corresponding increase of powers of concentration.

My husband was in an automobile accident a few months after I began therapy. As a result of this collision, his lungs, already weakened from chronic obstructive pulmonary disease, suffered severe bruising. He had never been in favour of alternative therapies, but his suffering was such that he agreed to let Kensen administer shiatsu therapy. After only one treatment, he said the relief he felt was nothing short of miraculous. We didn't know at the time he was also in an advanced stage of prostate cancer, diagnosed six months later during a general medical examination. He continued having regular shiatsu therapy until the time of his death in 1999, and it gave him enormous help in coping with all of the discomforts of two major illnesses. He looked forward to the days when he would have shiatsu therapy and was always able to fall into a deep, restful sleep following the treatments. I believe if shiatsu were at least partly subsidized by the government the overall benefit to people's health in treating existing problems and preventing future ones would be considerable, not to mention the resulting savings in medical costs.

– Jule Webb

"Shiatsu and My Experience of Late Pregnancy," May 2003
I married late, at 38, and when I turned 39 we decided to have a child. I miscarried, and after that we went to an infertility doctor to see if there was anything wrong. The doctor suggested that we be "aggressive with Mother Nature," meaning very expensive drugs and technical procedures like sperm washing, in vitro fertilization and intrauterine insemination, with the accompanying risk of premature and multiple births. My husband and I were repelled by the unnaturalness of all this. My husband suggested shiatsu treatments with Kensen Saito, who had previously helped him with many health problems. I underwent treatment with Kensen and subsequently delivered two healthy daughters naturally, one at age 41 and the second at age 43. When I look at my beautiful daughters, I always feel grateful to Kensen for helping me to conceive and carry to term two healthy babies in a natural and uncomplicated way.

– Lidia Costa

***

During my years of practice in Toronto, I have treated many patients in businesses of various kinds, who came to me because of the toll their lifestyle and work stress were taking on their body. One such client is Joanne Christopher, 46, who was a flight attendant for a major airline for 25 years, working mostly long overseas flights, which meant her body had to cope with time zone changes as well as lengthy hours of demanding physical work. Jet lag can throw our systems out, breaking into the natural rhythm of our body and disturbing the autonomic nervous system. That, in turn, affects the hormonal systems. Shiatsu helps bring our bodily systems back to their natural order and function. Joanne first came to me after reading about shiatsu in a

THE BENEFITS OF SHIATSU: PATIENT TESTIMONIALS

newspaper article. She was suffering from serious back problems and a badly herniated disc, as well as degenerated discs in her neck and numbness down the back of her leg. She came for weekly treatments to begin with, then gradually tapered off to monthly treatments. At one appointment, I asked Joanne why she continued to seek out regular shiatsu treatments:

"In my job, we push and pull very heavy trolleys," she told me. "After 20 years, most of us have some kind of back and neck problems, none of which is covered by our health plans. I was in traction for a while, and I've tried acupuncture and massage. They helped a bit. But my work continues to cause a lot of aches and pains, and my back problems are so bad that I can't afford for anyone to make a mistake on my back. When I have shiatsu on my leg, it's the only kind of treatment that brings back some feeling in my numb leg. This pressing on the points must help it; it certainly offers me temporary relief. The first time I carry a bag of heavy groceries, the numbness comes back, but I appreciate the time of relief. I'm so thankful for the feeling of extra energy shiatsu creates in me. It really helps me on overseas flights. I notice my feelings of relaxation and increased energy levels after a treatment. I'll stick it out for as long as I can afford it, and I wish I could afford treatments more often."

Another regular client of mine, Jennifer Hart, who is in her mid-30s, works in a highly stressful marketing job in the entertainment industry. Jennifer has been coming for regular shiatsu treatments for more than eight years and has a treatment every two months. She also sees a chiropractor regularly. Jennifer has upper back and neck problems aggravated by long periods of standing. She believes these problems originated with sports injuries and a car accident some years ago. Jennifer told me she has problems with her back and neck whenever she uses a computer or sits for any length of time. I asked her to comment on her treatments:

"I had tried massage and found it nice and relaxing but I didn't get any other benefits from it. The first time I came for shiatsu, I felt really strange and a little nauseous after the first half hour. I know that is really rare, but it's what I felt. But that evening, I found I could move better and I felt energy coming on me in full force. I understand that people aren't supposed to expect instant benefits from shiatsu, but I got them. Whenever I go for shiatsu, it takes away any stiffness I may have. I used to get tension headaches, but as long as I am having both chiropractic and shiatsu, I don't get the headaches the way I did. Keeping a regular schedule of shiatsu treatments really helps me. Once, when I got especially busy, I missed a couple of months. I felt a real difference when I started to go regularly again. My job is a demanding one, and I have more energy in the few days after a shiatsu treatment. Last year when I ran a marathon, I got a shiatsu treatment beforehand, and it made a huge difference in my energy. I found out recently I have a stomach problem called acid reflux, which is stress related. Through self-administered shiatsu and a change in my diet, I can stay off any medications. The shiatsu has been a tremendous benefit. For me, though, the main benefit of shiatsu is that it is truly a great stress reliever."

CREATION

CHAPTER 7

SHIATSU HELPS ATHLETES EXCEL

Shiatsu is a common way for Japanese boxing champions to stay in peak form long after you might expect that they would and to dispel physical problems that might stand in the way of winning. One inexperienced but talented young boxer named Kuniaki Shibata had back problems that were interfering with his progress. Tokujiro Namikoshi gave him treatments, sometimes without charging him, until the problems disappeared. Later, after he had gone on to become the world champion for his weight category in Mexico, Shibata returned to Tokyo to publicly thank Tokujiro for making it all possible for him. One of Toru's patients also became a world boxing champion: Fighting Harada, as he was called, was renowned for attaining the title of world champion in two categories during his career. When the great boxer Muhammed Ali was in New York, he arranged to have a shiatsu treatment from Tokujiro. When heavyweight champ George Forman came to Tokyo, he saw Toru for treatments. In 1974, when Ali and Forman were scheduled to fight each other in a classic boxing match in Ziele, Africa, the Tokyo press lined up father and son against each other, debating which one was better. Ali won, and Tokujiro's reputation as the ultimate master of shiatsu therapy stood.

Shiatsu and athletic training: a winning combination

Athletes young and old can greatly benefit from incorporating shiatsu into their train-ing programs. For the young, shiatsu aids physical development, both skeletal and muscular. For older athletes, regular shiatsu means fewer injuries and much greater ability to focus on the task at hand. Over the years, I have learned how to work best with athletes in many fields and how shiatsu can enhance their performance. I have also learned how important it is to tell my patients what the outcomes will be if they neglect their physical problem, not just how I can help them. It was the experience with Bill Caudill of the Toronto Blue Jays that drove that point home.

When I left Japan for North America, one of my dreams was to give shiatsu treatments to Hollywood stars, major league baseball players and executives of big companies. Bit by bit, that dream started falling into place. After I treated a Japanese

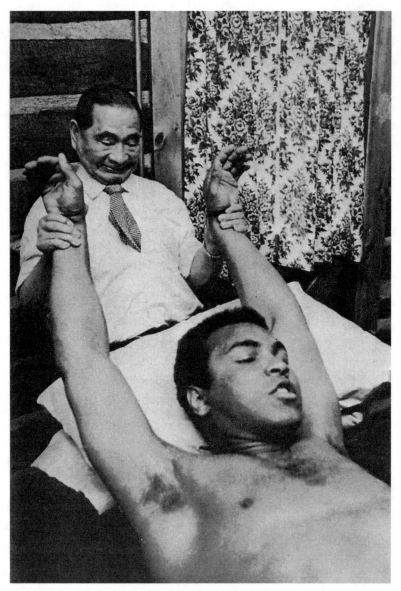

Tokujiro Namikoshi treating Muhammed Ali, 1973.

SHIATSU HELPS ATHLETES EXCEL

business executive one time, he gave me a note with the Japanese characters for "creation" written in calligraphy. I often stared at the piece of paper, considering what it meant in my life. Eventually, I started thinking that I wanted to have Olympic athletes and Hollywood stars among my patients. Sometimes people say that I do shiatsu for celebrities, but that's not quite true. I know that in some cases patients were already famous enough before I treated them, but in many more cases, patients have achieved great success in their fields after incorporating shiatsu into their lives.

The relationship between mind, body and spirit

I started to learn shiatsu when I was a university student. The motivation came from my interest in the as yet undeveloped notion of shiatsu and ability development. When I had a hands-on therapeutic treatment in my high school days, not only did it heal my body pain but it also helped me achieve higher marks in my studies and a new personal best in sports. I had been interested in conscious and subconscious awareness, meditation and relaxation techniques ever since I was an elementary school student, so I used to practise on my classmates and myself, but I felt that something was lacking. During that first hands-on treatment, I realized that not only is the therapy able to heal pain but it also draws out latent abilities and opens up many more possibilities. In shiatsu, I found my ideal therapy, along with an extension of my interest – the relationship between body, spirit and mind as well as the development of latent abilities. When I started learning shiatsu, I was an athlete at my university and also the coach of the long-distance relay race team at my former high school. I felt that learning shiatsu was useful for coaching sports. It may sound a little odd if I say I wanted to "create," but I got interested in "producing," and that was precisely where my ambition was headed. I had entered a stage when I wanted to prove to everyone that it was possible to develop their latent abilities through shiatsu. As it happened, the 13-year-old athlete Mary Fuzesi visited my clinic right around that time.

With young athlete Mary Fuzesi the night she placed 10th in the rhythmic gymnastics finals at the Seoul Olympics, 1988.

A young gymnast enters my life

Mary Fuzesi, a gymnast born in Budapest, Hungary, had terrible pain in her lower back when she arrived at my clinic with her mother. During the first treatment, I felt the potential of her athletic body – in fact, it reminded me of what it was like working with the Olympic gold medallist Lori Fung. I said to Mary's mother, "This girl will be a world-ranking gymnast." But she was too concerned about Mary's back pain to think about her daughter's athletic ambitions. It seemed to her that the pain was the result of extremely hard training, and she did not know whether she should let Mary continue in the sport. As I worked on Mary, I became aware that the back pain was associated with knee trouble. I was sure that it was treatable through shiatsu, and I felt that it would be a shame if she did not have the opportunity to explore her potential in rhythmic gymnastics when it was obvious to me that she could be a world-class athlete. I

SHIATSU HELPS ATHLETES EXCEL

told her mother that it was important for Mary to continue to have regular shiatsu treatments over the next little while. After several treatments, Mary's pain was ameliorated and she went off to compete in the Pan Am Games in Indianapolis, Indiana.

Mary came home with a silver medal and three bronze medals, including a bronze medal for being one of the top overall champions. Reporters marvelled that she was able to perform so well in spite of the back problem that had limited her training for two months. After the Games, Mary came for shiatsu regularly, and I talked to her about its benefits for athletes. It was obvious she had a very mature outlook for her age. One time, I decided to watch Mary take part in a competition in Toronto. While I was very impressed at her overall ability, I noticed she sometimes had trouble catching balls and ribbons as required in rhythmic gymnastics. In treatments afterwards, I made a point of working on her hands and arms. Whenever I work with athletes, I like to watch them perform. That way I can get a better understanding of their sport and a good idea of any weaknesses so I can help them improve in those areas. I watch which muscles and joints get the most stress and observe the athlete's relationship with coaches and family members, making a mental note if I see any particular pressure. Afterwards, I can tailor my shiatsu treatments to help them reach their maximum potential.

On the way to the Olympic Games

I started working with Mary in 1987, a pre-Olympic year. I had always been interested in the Olympics since boyhood and had childish dreams about going into pro sports or competing at the Olympics. Of course, I understood that Mary was only 13 and a junior and that Canada could only send two rhythmic gymnasts to the Olympics – Lori Fung and another senior gymnast. But the Olympics were on my mind. As I treated Mary one day, I told her that if she were to be selected for the Olympic team, I would go to Seoul with her and give her shiatsu there. The following spring, Toronto hosted the international Four-Continent Rhythmic Gymnastics Championship. I treated both Lori and Mary during the competitions. At the end, Lori was the champion in the senior division, and Mary was the champion in the junior division. They were both headed to the Seoul Olympic Games! Then, just one month before the Olympics, to everyone's shock Lori announced her retirement from the sport. A few days later, Mary and another athlete were named to the Canadian team.

Mary had just turned 14, and instead of going to the Olympics with Lori simply to get some Olympic experience, she was now the top figure on Canada's team. It was a lot of pressure for a young athlete. I remembered my pledge to accompany her to the Olympics if she made the Canadian team, and I meant to abide by it. I knew the Fuzesi family could not afford to pay for me, so I said I would pay my own fare. I will never forget the moment during the flight to Seoul when the captain announced he had just heard that Canadian Ben Johnson had won gold in the 100-metre race. The cabin erupted in cheering. When we landed, I went straight to the Olympic Village. Ben Johnson's photograph was everywhere in the Canadian Athletes' Village. Mary and her family greeted me. She was feeling very tired, so I gave her a treatment before going to my hotel. The next morning, Ben Johnson's picture was all over the television. I soon learned the disappointing news that he had tested positive for drugs and a scandal had erupted. When I got to the Olympic Village, all his photographs had been taken down.

I treated Mary, concentrating on her hands and arms, and off she went to participate in her first event. Before leaving Canada, Mary's coach had told me that if Mary made her best-ever showing, she could place 18th in the world. On that first day of competitions, she placed 16th among the top 20 gymnasts; all 20 could go to the Olympic finals. During the days following, she continued to perform very well, and at the end of the events, she had placed 10th in the world. That night, I thought she was the most charming 14-year-old on the earth. Because of her excellent performance at the Olympics, Mary was later named junior athlete of the year by the Sports Federation of Canada.

The experience at the Seoul Olympics stands out in my mind because it crystallizes the significance of shiatsu's role in athletics. Ben Johnson cheated and used performance-enhancing drugs. Mary achieved her best-ever performance completely drug-free. Shiatsu draws out the athlete's ability to perform at his or her peak without the use of drugs. It enables the body to perform at its very best. What a thrill that my own childhood dream to go to the Olympics had come true through shiatsu as well. Thanks to Mary's parents, who made arrangements for me, I went to the closing ceremonies, and when I saw the banners that read See You in Barcelona, I thought to myself, I certainly hope so.

I had the opportunity to help Mary during a major international gymnastics competition called The Brother Cup in Tokyo in 1989. It was also an opportunity for me to visit my relatives and friends there. More than 20 countries were represented, and the gold and silver medallists from the Seoul Olympics were competing. The number one Japanese gymnast, Erika Akiyama, was expected to take third place. There I was back in my homeland yet working to improve the chances of the Canadian gym-

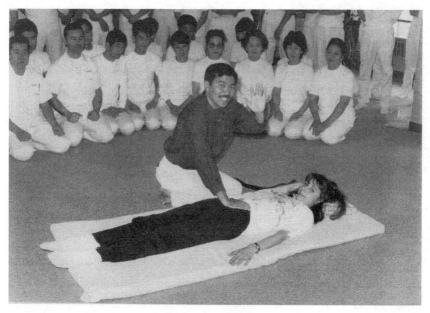

Demonstrating on Mary Fuzesi, Canadian rhythmic gymnastics champion, for a special lecture on sports shiatsu at the Japan Shiatsu College in Tokyo, May 1989.

nast. Mary came third in this meet, an excellent placing for her. I felt very proud that she had risen to the top in her country and then placed third in a major international event, all drug-free. Afterwards, I took her to visit the Japan Shiatsu College. Both Tokujiro and Toru were very pleased to welcome us. I gave lectures at the college on shiatsu and sports, discussing how it speeds up recovery from injury, eliminates fatigue related to training, prevents injury, improves neuromuscular coordination and enhances performance. Mary went on to win three gold medals, including the overall event at the New Zealand Commonwealth Games early in 1990.

A talented swimmer embraces shiatsu

My experiences of working with Mary, especially going to the Olympics, gave me a tremendous feeling of satisfaction. Shiatsu had not yet finished providing me with opportunities to help talented young athletes and even Olympic athletes. The year I opened my shiatsu academy to teach others the technique as I had learned it, there was a tall young fellow named Marcel Gery in my first class. He was physically in very good condition and I learned he was a member of the Canadian national swimming team. He had heard of my work at the Seoul Olympics and told me of his own background, including his defection from Czechoslovakia in 1986. He had been swimming since his boyhood; by the age of 15, this lad from the town of Smolenice had become one of the top swimmers in Czechoslovakia. Although he had hoped to go to the Olympics, his country decided to send a senior swimming team to the Moscow Games that year, so young Marcel knew he would have to wait for his chance. By the time he was 19, he was the top swimmer in the country and was excited about competing at the 1984 Olympics in Los Angeles. He looked to be a solid prospect for a silver medal there. It was unfortunate for him when the Soviet Union decided to boycott those Games and all the Eastern Bloc countries followed suit; Marcel missed his second chance to participate in the Olympics.

Two years later, when he was 20 years old, Marcel defected and came to Canada with his wife, Micheala, when they were supposedly on holiday in Yugoslavia.

With Marcel Gery (left) and Mark Tewskbury, two members of the bronze medal-winning men's relay swim team, Barcelona Olympic Games, 1992.

By the age of 23, he was Canada's butterfly stroke champion. The 1988 Olympic Games in Seoul lay ahead, but according to Canadian law he was not eligible to represent Canada because he had only lived in the country for two years and his application for an early citizenship hearing had been denied. Marcel once again sat at home and watched the Olympics on television, longing for the third time to be competing with the other top swimmers. Fate had not been kind to him about his dreams of going to the Olympics, but he still wasn't ready to give up. When he came to my school at age 25, he told me that he really wanted to pursue his ambition to be an Olympic swimmer, but he knew that Barcelona in 1992 would be his very last chance; he would then be 27. We had a chat about my approach to athletics through the drugless practice of shiatsu. I told him that shiatsu can help athletes maintain good health and reach their peak. Even if a person taking drugs wins, they are breaking the law and disrespecting fair play – and what do they gain from sports after their retirement? Nothing is going to be left. On the other hand, how much do athletes increase flexibility and durability through shiatsu? How much does it help release mental tension and enable them to do their best? It is what I call "sports shiatsu" that we research and practise to determine its benefits. I asked him if he took any performance-enhancing substances, and he assured me that he did not. He told me that when he was a young teenager in Czechoslovakia, an official from a government sports organization had visited his father one day and said that they wanted to put Marcel into a special training program. His father knew this meant a whole regimen of drugs, and he refused to talk any further to the official about it. He simply said no and stood by his decision.

Marcel had a good friend from boyhood who travelled with him to youth athletic competitions. His friend was a shot-putter and had an excellent overhand throw. After Marcel's friend got married, his wife had a baby that was born with severe deformities. Everyone close to the young family knew that the shot-putter had been on steroids and other drugs for years. It was clear that the baby's condition was a side effect of the father's use of artificial hormones over a long period of time. Marcel's friend was the national shot-put champion, but he and his family ended up paying a heavy price for that. Marcel told me he wholeheartedly agreed with my drugless approach to athletic excellence, so I pledged to do my very best for him in the two years we had leading up to the Barcelona Olympics and I said I believed that he could swim in the Games in 1992. Marcel had been suffering from agonizing muscle spasms in his back, which sometimes got so bad that he could hardly move. He was also having some respiratory trouble; sometimes while swimming, he would suddenly feel as if he could not breathe. I found as I treated him that his lower back was his particular physical weak spot. After a few shiatsu treatments, the breathing problems cleared up entirely and his back improved tremendously, so he was able to go on with his training. He said shiatsu not only relieved his back pain but also kept him relaxed and able to perform well. I discovered that part of the reason for his back pain was weight training; many young athletes experience similar problems. Sometimes coaches keep pushing them, ignoring their physical condition, but this can actually bring an abrupt end to a promising athletic career for some very talented athletes. Marcel did not have to give up his weight training, though, and he worked very well with his coach. Eventually, through shiatsu and stretching exercises, the lower back pain went away altogether. In December 1990, Marcel went to compete in the U.S.A. open swimming championships in Indianapolis. He was up against the Seoul Olympic gold medallist, Anthony Nesty of Surinam. Marcel swam very well, coming second to American Brian Alderman in the 100-metre butterfly, with Nesty coming third.

I had never been to a swim meet. In January 1991, there was a world swimming championship in Perth, Australia, and I decided to go to see Marcel swim, observe the atmosphere and gauge what approach was best to improve his chances. I find that with some sports an athlete is best off having the last shiatsu treatment three days before competing; with other sports, it is best to continue treatments right up to the night before the competition or even the day of the competition. Swimming for Canada, Marcel came fifth in the 100-metre butterfly. He also swam the butterfly lap for Canada's relay team and did very well. When he came home, he wrote a letter to the editor of the Shiatsu Diffusion Society's newsletter:

"I have been involved in competitive swimming for almost 17 years and through this period have experienced many treatments from different therapists all over the world. As an athlete, I am always looking for ways to improve my performance, both mentally and physically, for a major competition. Last year, I heard about the benefits of shiatsu therapy and was very curious to experience this method of relieving stress and fatigue and stimulating the body's natural healing power. Luckily for me, Kensen Saito, master of shiatsu, decided to accompany me to Australia for the Seventh World Aquatic Championships. Six weeks prior to this, because of muscle spasms in my back, I started receiving treatments on a regular basis. My back had been bothering me for a number of months. I experienced relief after three to four shiatsu treatments from Kensen. This was definite proof to me that shiatsu is effective. During the World Championships, I received four additional treatments. At this point, I was at my peak physical condition. I felt strong and loose, and my muscles and joints were very flexible. The complete motion of my butterfly stroke was quite easy to perform. Due to strategic error, I did not fully accomplish my goal. However, for the upcoming Olympics, I will continue to explore shiatsu as a means of enhancing my performance. Shiatsu is definitely the way to go."

Marcel then decided to go on to the World Cup swimming circuit in Europe to earn money for living expenses for himself, his wife and their baby boy. He swam very well and became the World Cup champion. In an exhibition meet, he beat Mark Spitz, the American who had won seven Olympic gold medals. Marcel also finished his training at the shiatsu academy and graduated from the one-year program. In July, after his graduation, he swam at the Pan Pacific meet in Edmonton. In the 100-metre butterfly heat, he achieved the second best time of his career: 53.89. He came second to American Matt Biondi, earning the silver medal. In November 1991, I was in Italy to attend the international shiatsu congress at the same time that Marcel was competing in Florence, so I went there to give him shiatsu treatments.

A long-time Olympic dream
Marcel wanted very much to be an Olympic swimmer, but he needed to be selected for the team. He was already 27, and Canada had another talented, world-ranking butterfly specialist in Tom Ponting of Calgary. In May 1992, Marcel went to Montreal for the Olympic selection meet. Before he went, he came to me for a treatment. I had determined just what the best possible treatment was, and that is what I gave him. On May 14, while I was teaching in my classroom, my office phone rang. I excused myself from the class, knowing it might be important news. It was Micheala Gery calling to

tell me that Marcel had won a tight race against Tom Ponting in the Olympic trials. After 12 years, Marcel's dream was finally going to come true: he was going to the Olympics! On the news that same night, there happened to be a broadcast about the death of Lyle Alzado, an NFL all-star football player who had continuously taken steroids in order to maintain his status; he had tragically died from a brain tumour caused by an overdose of the drug. The announcer told the public that the 43-year-old Alzado regretted exchanging his life for such stupidity and wished that the young people out there would rethink drug abuse.

I felt I had to do my very best shiatsu for Marcel, and so I boarded a plane to Barcelona, paying my own way. The day before my flight, my daughter, then nine years old, suddenly asked me, "Dad, why don't you do shiatsu on Japanese people when you're Japanese?" Unlike me, my daughter was born in Canada. I responded by asking her if she remembered Mary Fuzesi. I explained that Mary was born in Hungary and came to Canada when she was three years old with her parents. When she was still a junior athlete, she injured her back and came for a shiatsu treatment. At that time, I promised her that if she became an Olympic athlete I would accompany her to the Games. She worked very hard and became a Canadian champion and then an Olympic athlete. So, just as I had promised her, I went to Seoul and helped her. Then I explained to my daughter that Marcel was born in Czechoslovakia, but this time he was representing Canada. "I do not treat people according to their nationality," I explained. "I'll treat anyone who is working hard to achieve his or her dreams."

Living in Toronto, one meets people from many countries and backgrounds. The extent of this multicultural experience can never be undervalued. Those who left their country of birth and culture behind find similarities and share an understanding. Living in this multicultural environment, I felt that I was able to peel off a film that had accumulated on me unwittingly by living solely among Japanese people and in Japan's culture. I think it is culturally nourishing to live in a cosmopolitan society.

I greatly enjoyed the opening ceremonies of the Olympics, finding them quite exciting and energizing. Marcel's first heat came on July 27, and I gave him two shiatsu treatments leading up to that. He came second in his heat, beaten only by the world record holder, American Pablo Morales. The Olympic Village was extremely noisy night and day, and Marcel found himself unable to sleep. His coach gave him his hotel room the night before he was to swim, and I went there to treat him.

The United States has always been the dominant force in swimming, and the American team always took the first buses from the Olympic Village to the competition site on the day of a meet. They kicked Marcel off the bus on the day of his meet, but Pablo Morales intervened, saying that Marcel was a friend of his, so Marcel was able to stay on the bus with the American athletes. Because of this stroke of luck, he arrived in time for a shiatsu treatment before his final swim. His wife and mother were there to cheer him on, and I was also at the competition that evening. Pablo Morales won the gold medal. Marcel came sixth, which was a great disappointment to him since he knew these were his first and last Olympic Games. I wondered how to encourage him and keep his spirits up since he still had to swim the butterfly lap in the relay. The day before the relay, I was at a cocktail party in the hotel banquet room and started chatting with a Christian minister about Marcel's situation. The minister told me what the Bible says: In a race all the runners run, but only one will get the prize; each must run in such a way as to get the prize. Everyone who competes goes into strict training. They do it to get a crown that will not last; but we do it to get a crown that will last forever. These words encouraged me as I thought of Marcel, so I called him before the men's relay and tried to communicate some of my thoughts to him. He was feeling rather low since he had really wanted to go home with a medal; he had one more big job to do and he was ready to get on with it. On July 31, I sat with Micheala to watch the very last swimming event of the Games, the men's relay race. The first swimmer was backstroke specialist Mark Tewksbury, the golden boy of those Olympics. He swam very well, and Marcel performed at a very high level; the Canadian team won the bronze medal. In the end, Marcel had his medal to take home. Meeting the press afterwards, Marcel told them, "I have waited a long, long time for this. It's a dream come true."

SHIATSU HELPS ATHLETES EXCEL

Upon returning from the 1992 Barcelona Olympic Games, I was honoured to be among the Ontario Olympians who received an award from then premier Bob Rae and the minister of recreation.

To my amazement, I also ended up with an award for my Olympic experience. That September, I received a phone call from the Ontario Ministry of Recreation about a ceremony planned to present awards to Ontario's Olympians. I assumed I was being invited to watch Marcel receive an award, but I was told that I was to receive one myself. I felt proud and honoured to go to Queen's Park with the athletes, coaches and trainers to receive an award from then premier Bob Rae. It was a very happy day for me. I was thrilled to have been to the Olympics and to have helped make my patient's dreams come true – sharing in that happiness was enough. Now that I had an award myself, I felt I really had something to tell my boyhood friends, with whom I had dreamed of going to the Olympics and making a mark.

BE A DRAGON.

THE CLOUDS DRIFT

ON THEIR OWN

龍と成れ

雲自ずと来たる

CHAPTER 8
SHIATSU: A FRIEND TO ENTERTAINERS

One February night in 1956, Tokujiro Namikoshi was jolted awake by the telephone in his Tokyo home. It was Frank "Lefty" Odoul, one of his patients, the manager of the San Francisco Seals and also Joe DiMaggio's mentor. He was calling from the Imperial Hotel downtown and asked if Tokujiro would rush right over to the hotel to give a shiatsu treatment to an American film star. Marilyn Monroe, DiMaggio's new wife, had acute abdominal pain and needed help. They were in Tokyo on their honeymoon, before heading to Korea, where Marilyn would entertain the American troops. Tokujiro was still half asleep at the start of the phone call, but he soon snapped awake and assured Frank that he was on his way.

Tokujiro meets Marilyn Monroe

When he arrived at Room 205 of the Imperial Hotel, he found a pale Marilyn Monroe writhing in pain and moaning. He started shiatsu and soon determined to his satisfaction that the problem was not a serious disease or gallstones or anything that would require immediate medical attention. He found one spot on the lower part of her left shoulder blade that was really tense and stiff under his sensitive thumbs. He stayed on that point, pressing it repeatedly. Marilyn's body soon responded. Within 10 minutes, she relaxed completely and almost fell asleep. Tokujiro did a complete shiatsu treatment: neck and head, back and front and both sides of her body. The next day, the star called Tokujiro and asked for another treatment. He ended up being invited to the Imperial Hotel seven times to treat her. Tokujiro told Marilyn that his son was studying in Iowa and he wanted to send some money to him but it was very difficult to get U.S. dollars at that time. Marilyn paid for her treatment in Japanese yen but added five U.S. dollars to be sent to Toru in Iowa. Tokujiro has always regarded Marilyn Monroe and her enthusiasm for her treatments as the best advertisement shiatsu could have. Even long after she died, whenever Tokujiro travelled to Los Angeles, he always laid flowers on her grave.

Shiatsu takes centre stage

Shiatsu is effective in helping entertainers enhance their skills. I have great confidence in its benefits for performers of all kinds. In the same way I can prepare a rhythmic gymnast for a competition by concentrating on the arms and hands in a treatment, I can use shiatsu to make performers' hands and arms better able to communicate the feelings of their character. Shiatsu is extraordinarily effective in helping a performer's whole body become more expressive. It also dissipates the enormous stress that actors take into their body. Regular treatments help them remain calm and in control throughout a film shoot or during the demanding run of a play, so they perform at their best in spite of the horrendous pressures on them.

For television and movie actors in particular, shiatsu can significantly enhance the appearance of their face. I have studied the distribution of nerves in the face: the autonomic nervous system and the cranial nerves. Shiatsu regulates and balances these nervous systems. It relaxes them. It gives the face a natural glow and enhances the attractiveness of the features. In any field in which appearance is critical, including acting and modelling, shiatsu can help the individual put his or her best face forward. I have observed this time and time again, having treated a number of entertainers, some of them very well known and respected in their fields.

In the early '80s, the actress Lenore Zann came to see me about stress problems in her neck. I understood that her profession was a stressful one and was happy to work with her to try to relieve her problem. After a few treatments, the problem improved considerably. She also found the regular treatments very helpful in coping with the demands of her career. In the summer of 1993, Lenore was making a short film with the actor Henry Czerny, who played the part of a stressed-out executive. At Lenore's instigation, the director asked me to perform shiatsu in the film and I agreed at once. It was great fun for me. When it was screened, I took my daughters to see it. At the end, my youngest asked, "Where was Dad?" Her sister replied, "Didn't you recognize Dad's hands on the man's shoulders?" I had to laugh – the rest of me had ended up on the cutting room floor!

Babyface stars James Gallanders and Lenore Zann with me at the Cannes Film Festival, 1998.

Lenore has been a loyal patient for many years. I have enjoyed assisting as her shiatsu therapist and have long appreciated her talent as a film actress and as a vocal artist. In 1998, Lenore's dream of going to the Cannes Film Festival was fulfilled when Atom Egoyan's Babyface was screened there; Lenore had the leading role. I was thrilled for her.

In 1988, soon after Lenore finished filming a TV movie called Love and Hate in Western Canada with the gifted Brent Carver, she opened at the Poor Alex Theatre in Toronto in a highly controversial play called Unidentified Human Remains and the True Nature of Love. I went to cheer her on, and backstage she introduced me to Brent. Shortly thereafter, he started coming to my clinic for regular treatments to help him deal with the high stress that so often accompanies a successful career in the entertainment field. Over the years, he has become a good friend and a great fan of shiatsu. I have followed his career with admiration as he travels the world to play demanding roles. Whenever possible, I give him shiatsu treatments to help cope with stress and to enhance his wonderful talents.

In 1992, Brent landed the lead role in the play Kiss of the Spider Woman, which opened in Toronto that summer. Like an athlete going into training for a crucially important competition, Brent went into serious training for his new role. For most Shakespearean actors, it is a huge challenge to take on the major role in a big American musical requiring lots of singing and dancing. Brent pushed himself, putting his heart and soul into doing his very best with this show. He felt a great sense of commitment and gave all his focus to the play. He followed a rigidly controlled diet, exercised regularly and came for shiatsu twice a week. I respected his dedication and used our time to help him prepare to do his best. When the show opened in Toronto, it was an instant hit. It won rave reviews, and audiences loved it. After a highly successful run in Toronto, it moved on to London. Early in 1993, I was in England promoting shiatsu while Brent was there. He had been nominated for a Laurence Olivier Award for his performance. Before I went to see the show in London's West End, I gave Brent a shiatsu treatment. He was especially grateful because he had discovered that what is known as shiatsu in England is more like Chinese massage. He hadn't been able to find a treatment as effective as Japanese shiatsu. As I worked on Brent's body that day, I found that his arms and hands needed a lot of attention, so I focused on those areas in particular. Later, the Japanese practitioners I was travelling with accompanied me to the show. We enjoyed it very much, and Brent was wonderful. As we made our way back to our hotel, one of my colleagues asked if Brent had been the actor I had treated that day. I said that he was. He told me that he had found Brent's arms and hands to be so extraordinarily expressive that he had identified him as the one who must have had shiatsu before the show, and he felt he knew which parts of the body I had concentrated on that day.

After his great success in London, Brent headed back across the Atlantic. The play was finally going to open on Broadway. Before he went to New York, he came for a treatment in preparation for this important and challenging experience. I asked him how he felt about going to New York, and he told me that it felt as if he were facing the dragon. I was especially struck by this comment because it reminded me of my favourite poem, which translates literally from Japanese as: "Be a dragon. The clouds drift on their own." It means that you must do your best and give it all you have, then everything else will fall into place. I told Brent about the poem and he liked it a lot. He repeated to himself, "Be a dragon." Soon it was time for him to head off to Broadway. Less than two months after the opening, Kiss of the Spider Woman received a Tony nomination, and Brent was nominated for Best Actor. He told me that the Tony Awards were to be announced on June 6. That happened to be a special day for me because it would mark the 14th anniversary of my arrival in Canada. On June 6, I watched the awards show on television and was thrilled when Brent's name

Lenore Zann, Brent Carver and I attend a reception at the Four Seasons Hotel, Toronto, on opening night of Kiss of the Spider Woman, 1992.

was called as the winner of the Best Actor Award. It felt like winning a gold medal at the Olympics. Later, I went to New York to see the show and I wrote down the "Be a dragon" poem for him. He was very happy to receive it and put it in a place of honour beside his Tony Award in his dressing room.

Talking golf with Canada's songbird

In 1996, one of my patients, a woman who makes her living as a housekeeper, asked if I could do a house call. I explained to her that I very seldom go out to do treatments and would only do so in the case of a very serious problem, if someone were in the hospital in great need of a treatment or if a person had a highly compelling reason why coming to my shiatsu academy was not possible. She told me that her employer wanted a treatment but was a celebrity and would not feel comfortable sitting in a waiting room being stared at. She had once been stalked by a fanatic admirer and the experience had made her wary about public places. I asked what she did for a living, and my patient told me her employer was a singer named Anne Murray. The name rang a bell, but I am not very good at recognizing celebrities' names. I told my patient that I was busy teaching my classes but that at the end of the semester I would be willing to give her employer a treatment in her home.

When Anne Murray called, I agreed to see her on a Monday morning, and she gave me her address in a Toronto suburb. When I arrived, I discovered a beautifully landscaped property and a spacious, light-filled house. Anne greeted me and led me past her indoor swimming pool to the living room, where I was to give her a treatment. She had an exercise mat set out for that purpose. She told me she did aerobic workouts using the same mat. I asked her what other exercise she enjoyed, and she told me she played less tennis than she used to but she was playing a lot of golf. I was pleased to be able to tell her that shiatsu is especially helpful for golfers. A lot of players report their lowest score after a shiatsu treatment. In fact, one of my instructors shot a hole in one after a session.

Anne asked me to explain what shiatsu is and how it works. She did not have one of her frequent runs in Las Vegas coming up and she expected to be in town for some time, so we arranged to meet every Monday. Anne seemed quite excited about the idea of improving her golf game through shiatsu. I explained that one treatment would not lead to a hole in one; the improvement would be less dramatic but probably noticeable. Golf requires focus and concentration, two things that can be sharpened through shiatsu treatments. Since I had driven to Anne's house instead of taking a taxi, she gave me one of her CDs in lieu of transportation money. I listened to it later and recognized "Snowbird." Finally, I realized who she was! During the week between treatments, I told my mother about the CD, and she informed me that my 79-year-old aunt in Japan was a big Anne Murray fan. Anne had mentioned to me that she had toured Japan once.

The first time I gave Anne a treatment I noticed some stiffness in one of her elbows and her shoulders and back. When I returned for the second treatment, I found quite an improvement, and she mentioned that her shoulder pain had lessened. When I returned for the third treatment, she was waiting excitedly for me at the door to tell me she had scored 86 in a recent golf game, a personal best and the first time she had broken 90. I gave her five treatments over the course of the summer, then we had to discontinue because I was travelling to Peru and Anne was heading on tour to promote a new album. The last time I saw her, I brought along a copy of her new CD and asked her to autograph it for my aunt in Japan. She wrote my aunt's name and signed her own. That November, when I travelled to Japan, I made a point of paying my aunt a visit. At age 79, she was still working as a secretary for an American insurance company and wasn't planning to retire until the end of that year. She was born in Canada and always told me how proud she was of my success as a shiatsu therapist in Canada. She was even more impressed to learn that her nephew had given shiatsu treatments to the famous Anne Murray. She was very happy about the autographed CD.

More award-winning performances

Another long-time client and talented entertainer who is a hit with my friends in Japan is Toronto-based actor Lally Cadeau. Lally enjoys a distinguished career in live theatre and television and was hugely successful in the popular television series Road to Avonlea. The Japanese are great fans of Anne of Green Gables, and the Road to Avonlea series was very popular there. Lally first heard about my clinic from her sister-in-law, who had been impressed with shiatsu herself. Lally lived in the neighbourhood and decided to give shiatsu a try in 1989. She derived so many benefits from her first treatment that she continued and has come on and off over the years ever since, especially when she feels the need to loosen up her body. Lally has scoliosis, a curvature of the spine. It's not uncommon in women and can be very painful. Shiatsu relieves the pain caused by scoliosis and helps all her muscles work better. She finds that it lifts her spirits and gives her a feeling of well-being. As she says, shiatsu makes her "feel taller, straighter and better balanced." Lally was nominated for a Gemini Award for best supporting female actor over a period of several years, but the award always eluded her. In 1995, she was nominated instead in the best female actor category for her work in Road to Avonlea. I was thrilled when she won. It was much deserved. And she received another award that year: since opening my shiatsu academy, we have presented an annual Shiatsu Academy Award to a person connected to the academy who has achieved an important goal; Lally was named the winner that year. The award was presented at the 12th international shiatsu conference in Toronto. My Japanese colleagues enjoyed seeing Lally receive it as they knew her from the Avonlea series.

In good voice

Another acclaimed actor client of mine is Brian Stokes Mitchell. Stokes, as he likes to be called, lives in New York, but he came to Toronto in 1996 to rehearse for the musical Ragtime, which was opening at the Toronto Ford Centre for the Performing Arts. Stokes played the lead role of Coalhouse Walker, and his beautiful wife, Allyson

Tucker, was in the ensemble. In the theatre community, word had been spreading for a few years that my staff and I treated many actors. We often have several members of a large company, such as Kiss of the Spider Woman or Mamma Mia, as regular clients. When Stokes and Allyson arrived in Toronto to start rehearsing for Ragtime, he heard about my work from his colleagues and decided to give shiatsu a try.

Stokes had knee trouble and back pain. His demanding role required him to dance on a raked stage, as well as to sing and act. A raked stage makes it easier for the audience to see all parts of the play, but it's pretty tough on the performers to dance on those surfaces. Stokes came for regular shiatsu treatments during the rehearsal period and managed to keep the pain at bay even while he was making tough demands on his body. The afternoon before opening night, he came for a treatment and asked me to concentrate on making his voice the best it could be for all the singing he had to do in front of a bank of critics and the opening night audience. I did my best in the area of his vocal cords, and when he left I felt confident that he was ready to give a splendid performance. In the papers the following day, the critics raved about the show, and several of them complimented Stokes on his strong, clear voice. He was very pleased, and so was I. Stokes was so happy with the effects shiatsu had on his knees, back and voice that he came for regular treatments throughout Ragtime's Toronto run.

One afternoon when Stokes was leaving after his appointment, Brent Carver was sitting in the waiting area for his appointment right after. It pleased me to be able to introduce these two fine actors, both of whom were benefiting from shiatsu. Brent Carver had already won his Tony then. When I introduced Stokes, I said, "Stokes is going to win Best Actor in the upcoming Tony Awards." I was sure that Stokes would win it soon.

For my mother's 83rd birthday, I took her to see Ragtime. After the show, we visited the dressing rooms, and Stokes and Allyson showed us around backstage. My mother really enjoyed it, especially seeing the hundreds of costumes. Afterwards, Stokes and Allyson drove us back to my mother's house. When we were about to get out of the car, Stokes said to my mother, "You must know this already, but your son is the best shiatsu therapist in the world." In a card he sent me later, he said he could see that I had gotten what he called my "wonderful spirit" from my mother. That was very meaningful to me.

Stokes continued to have shiatsu treatments until he had to leave for Los Angeles with the Ragtime company to open the show in that city. He let me know that my treatments continued to be a great help in reducing the pain in his knees and back. I was glad of that because I know that musicals are extremely demanding. The actors have to give their all, both physically and emotionally, through eight shows a week for many months.

Brian Stokes was nominated for a Tony Award for Best Actor for his role in Ragtime, but unfortunately the award eluded him. Eventually, in 2000, he was nominated again, this time for Kiss Me Kate, and he won. Brent Carver and Brian Stokes Mitchell were both nominated for the Tony for Best Actor six times over 10 years on Broadway, and each won the award once. It has been one of the greatest joys in my life to have become their friend and to have helped them as their shiatsu therapist.

Backstage at New York's Martin Beck Theatre with Brian Stokes Mitchell during the Broadway run of Kiss Me Kate, 2002.

THE HEART OF SHIATSU IS LIKE

A MOTHER'S LOVE

PRESSING THE HUMAN BODY

STIMULATES THE FOUNTAINS OF LIFE

指圧の心母心
おせば生命の泉わく

CHAPTER 9

WHAT YOU LEARN AS A SHIATSU PRACTITIONER

Shiatsu is a splendid profession to take up in this age of high technology. A good shiatsu practitioner can never be replaced by a machine. It is wonderful to experience the inner satisfaction of having a patient go home recovered, but it is also necessary for a shiatsu practitioner to consider how to cope when a patient dies. Death cannot be avoided; however, anything you can do to help a dying person up until the end of his life is beneficial. I have performed shiatsu on the abdomen of a friend dying of cancer, and he found it comforting. I tell my students not to be depressed or disappointed if they cannot cure people: we need to realize that we cannot help 100 per cent of the patients we see. Sometimes we will get good results, but other times nothing can be done. We can help most people to some degree, but it is important to remain somewhat philosophical about how much we can do.

I do not encourage my students to give shiatsu when a patient appears to have undiagnosed cancer, but I do encourage them to send the patient to his family physician if they feel any irregularity during a treatment. If it is cancer and the patient undergoes surgery, a practitioner can give treatments after the operation or during the chemotherapy or radiation. Chemotherapy and radiation are very hard on the body, so the patient suffers a lot during this time. Shiatsu can ease the patient's discomfort to some degree. If the cancer is inoperable and has spread so far that nothing can be done to stop it, a therapist can help the patient find inner peace through shiatsu. Touch is an important factor. An understanding of death is important for people in the health care field.

Be sure it's the real thing

Shiatsu is only able to help the body do what it is capable of, and not every person who hangs up a sign offering shiatsu has been adequately trained in the methods developed by Tokujiro Namikoshi. So-called "shiatsu" is practised in many countries around the world, but I do not know what some people who call themselves shiatsu practitioners are doing. There are still far too many people practising what they claim is shiatsu, but it is not true shiatsu at all. It annoys me to be asked what kind of shiatsu I practise. People talk about Zen shiatsu and meridian shiatsu, but these have nothing to do with the shiatsu that was recognized by the Japanese health ministry in 1955. True shiatsu is not based on the 14 meridian lines in the Chinese medical philosophy, and it is not administered with elbows, knuckles or knees. The true shiatsu practitioner uses only thumbs, fingers and palms as these areas contain many sense receptors. Tokujiro always taught safe and effective techniques. Because it is a natural way of working with the body, it takes time to obtain results. Patients almost always want to see fast results; they are often looking for a quick fix. Sometimes a quick fix makes them worse and sometimes it does nothing. There are no magic bullets.

Leading a practice class at the Shiatsu Academy in Toronto, 1996.

Patience is a prerequisite

Often it is difficult for people who are suffering to be patient, although patience is what is needed. They have one or two treatments of one kind, then give up and go on to something else. They do not realize that they cannot gain anything that way. The body needs time to start to heal. Patients may make unreasonable demands of shiatsu and complain when their expectations are not met. I had one patient who was quite a difficult case. He had suffered pain for several years in his neck, shoulders and back, he experienced frequent dizziness and noise in the ears, and he had high blood pressure. He said he could not lie down without three pillows. His wife sent him to me and he asked if I could help him. I told him frankly that if I could make him completely better I should get the Nobel Prize but that I would try to use shiatsu to improve some of his symptoms. He came three times. Every time he came, he complained constantly while I would try to find some area of improvement. At first he thought the pain in his neck was worse, then he thought it had eased. He thought perhaps the noise in his ears had lessened a bit. But he spent his whole visit complaining. When he asked me whether I got tired working so hard during his treatment, I told him I only got tired of hearing him complain all the time.

A shiatsu practitioner has to be patient enough to listen to complaints. It's just part of the job. Many people you treat will keep silent about their good results but refer friends two or three years later. You just have to accept it; it comes with the territory. But there are also patients who openly express their appreciation for the help you have given, and that is very gratifying. I have a patient who underwent an operation for colon cancer three years ago. He had chemotherapy and tried to watch his diet afterwards but gained a great deal of weight and also had a problem with gas pains. When he came for his second treatment, he told me that after his first treatment he went around all day with the sense that something was missing. He had the same feeling all the next day too. He finally realized that it was the pain that was missing. He told me that he really appreciated the freedom from pain and remembered that in his childhood a teacher had once remarked on what a wonderful feeling it is to have pain go away.

For the treatment to be effective, the practitioner must be totally focused on helping the patient. There is a trust between practitioner and patient. Your hands and your mind are connected. If your mind is not with your hands, the patient will feel that. This can be difficult for a shiatsu practitioner. If you are worrying about your personal problems or thinking about what to have for dinner, you cannot be effective. You really need to concentrate on the patient's well-being.

Positive thinking is one of the key elements of healing. It is important to recognize any change – even a small one – in a patient's body after a shiatsu treatment. A student who worked with me once mentioned a patient who came for a series of treatments. After a few treatments, she felt a definite change in the patient's body, but he kept complaining. I often see this. The patient clings to the old state of mind. There can be a time lag as the information passes from body to mind. The healing can be happening on the physical side, but the mind is still occupied with the pain or discomfort. It takes time to realize the difference. It is similar to the situation you occasionally see in high-level sports: a player will have a serious physical injury like a fracture and still go out there and excel. That is just another kind of delay in the message getting from the body to the mind. Shiatsu helps us be more aware of ourselves. We think we know our body, but we are actually disconnected from it a lot of the time. Often we are not sharp enough to sense what is happening in our body. If we develop a stronger sense of our body, it helps us take better preventive care of ourselves. People in their 80s and 90s who have Alzheimer's disease do not appear to think or feel anything. They seem to be unaware of their own misery and unafraid of facing death.

At certain times, the body sends the brain information when something is changing. Pain is a kind of message. When some people feel pain, they go to the doctor to check it out. Others ignore it until it is too late and nothing can be done. Having shiatsu treatments is an opportunity for the patient to become more aware of his body. If something is not normal in a particular area, he starts to sense it. The awareness is at the conscious level but also goes to the subconscious level so that the

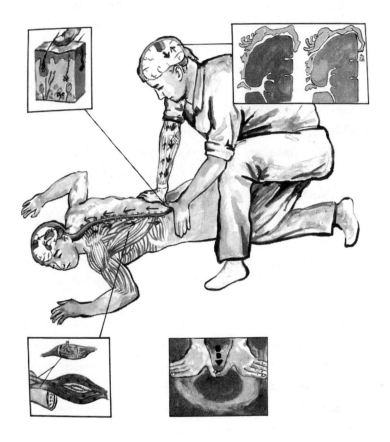

Both diagnosis and treatment occur simultaneously at the pressure point.

brain can start to send the proper healing aids – sufficient hormones, natural painkillers, oxygen or nutrients – to correct or heal that part. The same kind of thing can happen through yoga or stretching exercises. You can feel certain muscles and are aware of any irregularity; at the same time, yoga triggers the body's methods of treating the problem. But with shiatsu, this sensibility is much stronger than it is with yoga or stretching. People who have suffered for a long time sometimes know instinctively after their first treatment that shiatsu is what they have been looking for.

As shiatsu practitioners, we are aware of the sufferings and the joys of our patients. We deal with some of the most basic and critical elements of life in our practice. To be a good practitioner, it is necessary to think about these things. What is the aim of life for the individual? If we are not joyful, we don't have much of a life. We should all strive to have as much joy and happiness as possible. Each of us experiences some good moments, some good times. Some people have a lot of joy and others have very little, but everyone should seek it. Creativity is one way to find joy. That's certainly true for a patient of mine who came to Canada from Japan at the age of 75. Now in his 80s, he still paints, which is his passion, and he really enjoys life.

The practitioner-patient partnership

I do not know the physiological reasons why, but shiatsu opens up people's creativity. When I treat someone, it is like cultivating a plot of land and leaving it ready for the creative seed of the patient's choice. In entertainers, I have seen how a shiatsu treatment can improve performance. That appears to be the case for other creative activities as well. The best results come when the practitioner and the patient are in agreement about their goal and work together. The goal is health, but it is not a one-way street. The practitioner works as hard as possible to get the patient moving in a healthy direction, but the patient needs to be willing to do what is necessary to facilitate that. We must explain to patients looking for the instant miracle cure that shiatsu is not that. It is, instead, a process. Patience and understanding are required to participate in that process. Patients need to understand that time is necessary and that they must have a strong will and a keen desire to be healthy. They need to change, some-how, the parts of their lifestyle that led to their illness, perhaps by committing to a healthy diet and giving up smoking. They might even need to change their work situation or their own attitudes if that is the way to gain real health. People coming for health maintenance shiatsu treatments do not have to make a lot of changes in their lives but just maintain the healthy habits they have built up.

"Health care" versus "sick care"

We need to start distinguishing between "health care," that is, how to keep people healthy, and "caring for the sick," or how to treat people when they are ill. Today's medicine is focused on caring for the sick, and medical technology is developed for this approach: CT scans, laser operations and artificial joints, for example. Health care is a more educational field and has two main components: building up the body through good nutrition; and stress management, including exercise. These two elements go hand in hand in health care education.

What makes people ill? Viruses and bacteria are, of course, factors but they are over-emphasized. Preventable factors are not given enough attention. The more chemicals we put into our body, the more complex the new diseases will be. The chemical war against disease is over and we have lost! New approaches to health are needed. We must find out how to keep people in a healthy balance, a state of homeostasis. Stress is the enemy of homeostasis. Stress management helps us maintain homeostasis. Exercise, yoga and tai chi all contribute to maintaining hormonal and immune system balance.

The nervous system, endocrine system and immune system are based in the centre of the brain. Achieving a peaceful state in that part of the brain is the key to balancing the body. If that part of the brain is happy, the rest of the body is healthy. The effects even reach the subconscious level. Sometimes we think that the subconscious level is out of our reach, an uncontrolled place. Through shiatsu, we can send messages straight to the subconscious. The skin, which is the body's largest sense organ, and the brain cells were originally the same part of the embryo; one part developed into the skin and the other part became the brain. So skin-to-skin contact is like brain-to-brain contact or even spirit-to-spirit contact. A healing spirit is critically important in a practitioner, and the patient needs to be open to healing. In part, the healing can come about through a spiritual exchange. To send a message to the subconscious level, shiatsu uses thumb pressure, which travels through the sensory nervous system to the spine. The messages ascend the spine through neurons to the thalamus. From there, the message goes to the cerebral cortex and the conscious level.

The thalamus, hypothalamus and pituitary are all very close to each other in a linked system, so shiatsu's message-sending influences them all. The hypothalamus starts to produce hormones, which stimulate the pituitary gland, which in turn produces other hormones that are sent through the body to other glands. Quite often there can be a time lag between the shiatsu treatment and the pain relief. The messages set off chemical changes, but the hormone glands have no ducts; they are isolated in many parts of the body, so the hormones must travel through the bloodstream. Some hormones go into the bloodstream and take longer than the nerve reaction to reach the target areas. Sometimes a patient may feel a reaction the day after the treatment, then be highly energized the following day. That is nature taking a little time about these things. If a patient has suffered with a physical problem for a long period of time, then the link between the nervous system and the endocrine system will have been inactive for a long time. One or two treatments cannot turn that around, but there is always a possibility, if the right messages are being sent to the right places, that change may happen over time. Sometimes the cerebral cortex is completely occupied by the awareness of pain; it takes a while for messages of healing to come in from the subconscious. It is rather like the development of any ability in a person.

Shiatsu respects the rule of the body's own healing mechanism. If there is a healing system there, shiatsu will use it. Using the body's own healing mechanism is natural, causes no harm and doesn't burden the health care system with huge costs.

WHAT YOU LEARN AS A SHIATSU PRACTITIONER

As I said earlier, governments spend a lot of money on health care, but what they are really spending it on is care for the sick. If they could just turn that around and spend it on true health care, they would save money, improve people's health and nurture a more productive society. With the massive use of medications, more and more people end up depressed. With shiatsu, more and more people would feel uplifted and be healthier. That is because shiatsu brings to life the systems that make people feel happier. Mood change is one of the roles of hormones, and their production is stimulated by shiatsu.

The healing touch

There are some elements of shiatsu that are important for a capable practitioner to keep in mind, such as temperature and pressure level. In practising shiatsu, hand temperature is very important. Cold fingers can cause stress instead of promoting relaxation. Warm hands communicate reassurance, health and relaxation. Optometrists have a scale to measure how far we can see when testing our vision. Doctors have ways to measure how well we heal, which are recorded on a hospital chart while a patient recovers. We need a measure for the touch of skin. If I apply the same amount of pressure on the skin of three different patients, one will say "ouch," another will not feel it at all, and a third will feel good. Learning how much pressure to apply for each individual is an important skill the practitioner has to develop. No machine can ever replace this function. There are 1,000 different levels of pressure and a practitioner needs to understand all of them. It takes a lifetime to truly master this.

I recall one patient who came to me to try to relieve her shoulder and back pain; to her surprise, she stopped having migraines while she was in treatment. Someone who comes to have a sore shoulder treated and continues to come regularly will often say a year later, "You know, I used to have cramps in my legs at night but recently I realized I have not had one since I started coming here." Blood circulation is always improved after a shiatsu treatment, and that can have many benefits. Keeping the circulation system healthy is vitally important. Practitioners need to work with a patient to achieve good circulation, but we must also emphasize the need for a healthy diet and regular exercise. A high-fat diet causes plaque to attach to the arteries. Exercise also contributes to a healthy circulatory system, particularly the veins. During exercise, movement squeezes the veins through muscular contraction, sending the blood flowing back to the heart. It is imperative that practitioners discuss stress levels with their patients. Stress affects the nerves, and shiatsu works wonders for the nervous system.

The most precious gift we have is life. To believe in the life force and natural healing powers within us brings about healing. The most important treasure we can discover is the life force within us. To be able to understand the marvels of this life force is to understand the importance of our existence. This helps us understand others and appreciate that their lives are just as important as our own. When we can understand the environment and universe, we can understand the coexistence of the inner and outer parts of our skin, which separate us from the world outside our body – that is, the harmony between the pulse of a living organism's inner space and the rhythm of the universe. How can we be healthy when we pollute the environment and consume chemical drugs?

LIVE A HAPPY LIFE WHILE GIVING HAPPINESS TO OTHERS

人に喜びを与え
自分も喜び生きる

CHAPTER 10
THE INTERNATIONAL SCENE

I truly believe that if shiatsu were practised around the world it would be a better place in which to live. There would be less stress and less fighting. Society would be healthier overall. When I was considering this 15 years ago, I became impatient at how slowly shiatsu was spreading and told my teacher, Tokujiro Namikoshi, that at this speed, it would take 200 years for shiatsu to spread to all parts of the world. But Tokujiro believed that international recognition of shiatsu would come much faster than that. He was right. Since then, I have travelled much of the world for the cause of shiatsu, flying back and forth often between Canada and Japan and visiting many different places in Europe and the United States. My first trip to Europe was in November 1991, to attend the international shiatsu congress in Rome, Italy, hosted by Rudy Palombini, who had nearly 25 years of experience. Rudy used to be a masseur and worked with many topnotch athletes, including marathon runner Abebe Bikila, an Olympic gold medallist. Rudy was the official masseur of the Italian Olympic team and came to Tokyo in 1964 for the Summer Games. He had heard about Japanese shiatsu before he left Rome for Japan and was looking forward to meeting a master of shiatsu. During his spare time in Tokyo, he visited the Japan Shiatsu School and was treated by Tokujiro. Rudy was so impressed with the technique that he switched from massage to shiatsu right away. He trained under Tokujiro and started to practise in Rome.

Sights set on South America

Due to the tragic and unexpected death of Toru Namikoshi in May 1994, we cancelled a seminar planned that year in Peru. Although Tokujiro had travelled to many places to give shiatsu workshops, he regretted that he had not yet been to any South American countries. It had become a dream of his to go there.

In Peru, interest in shiatsu dates back more than 20 years, to the time when a Japanese man living in Peru became very sick and tried many remedies without results. He asked a relative in Japan to send him a book about shiatsu and he followed the information to learn self-shiatsu. Gradually, he regained his health and strength. On a trip to Japan, he met Tokujiro Namikoshi, and when he returned to his home in Peru, he founded a shiatsu hobby group. They repeatedly invited Tokujiro to visit Peru, but it never came about. Some years later, the Peruvian ambassador, Victor Aritomi, visited Japan and had a shiatsu treatment from Toru Namikoshi; the method impressed him greatly. He told Toru that there was a group of people in Peru anxious to have a shiatsu seminar take place there, and Toru responded by planning one for 1994. Because of his death, the seminar did not take place. The following year when I was in Tokyo, a man from the Peruvian embassy came to the college for a shiatsu treatment. He said the Peruvian enthusiasts were still keen to host a seminar and asked what I thought about the idea. I replied that we were having the international shiatsu meeting in Toronto in 1995, but perhaps the following year we could go to Peru. So the shiatsu hobby group, with the help of the embassy, organized a 1996 seminar. It felt right to me; the last thing Toru and I had talked about before his death was a shiatsu seminar in Peru. I was glad that we could fulfill this goal. It was also an opportunity for Tokujiro to finally take his dream trip to South America. To attend the Peru seminar, he flew from Tokyo to Los Angeles, Los Angeles to Miami, and Miami to Lima. It was quite a strenuous journey for a 91-year-old man.

This was the first international shiatsu seminar in South America. Shiatsu had already been recognized as an officially approved therapy by the Peru health ministry, although there was no official school yet. The shiatsu group in Peru had been practising shiatsu very effectively in Peruvian hospitals for years. There is a substantial Japanese community in Lima, and the shiatsu seminar attracted a large number of enthusiastic people; the morning we arrived, there were people lined up long before we even got there. Matsuko and Takashi Namikoshi, Toru's widow and son, gave very informative presentations at the seminar. The audience really seemed to enjoy it, and we went away feeling gratified that the first international shiatsu seminar in South America had been such a great success. When I immigrated to Canada from Tokyo in 1979, it never for a moment crossed my mind that I might go to Peru. Now I was being given the opportunity to share the dreams of my teachers, Tokujiro and Toru Namikoshi, and to share in the happiness of the people in Peru who had waited so

The shiatsu seminar at the Japanese Cultural Centre in Peru, 1996. From left: Shigeru Onoda, me, Tokujiro Namikoshi, Takashi Namikoshi and Fulvio Palombini.

long to have such a seminar, as well as those who responded to it with great enthusiasm. This experience made me happy beyond anything I had ever imagined. Helping people through shiatsu really does give me great joy.

After the seminar, I travelled to Machu Picchu with Shigeru Onoda of Spain. We have both promoted shiatsu outside of Japan. It had been two years since Toru passed away. During the trip, I listened to Onoda's great devotion to shiatsu in Spain. I was very encouraged by him.

A close call prompts a sense of mission

Snow was falling in the dark during the early hours of December 27, 1996, as I drove east along the Queen Elizabeth Way from Niagara Falls towards Toronto and home. Beside me in the passenger seat was my tenant, a Japanese boy. I was staying in the left lane, driving about 110 kilometres an hour, and was gauging that we would be home in about 20 minutes when I suddenly had one of the greatest shocks of my life. The car hit a patch of treacherous black ice. I lost control and the car slid across three lanes to the right, hit the guardrail and bounced back to the left again before coming to a stop in the middle lane. I told my tenant to get out of the car right away; we both headed to the other side of the guardrail for safety's sake. The first thing I realized was that I was still alive. I then tried to move my thumbs and fingers, so crucial for my work in shiatsu. I was relieved to find that I still had sensation in my hands, but my right arm from the elbow to the wrist was swollen and bruised. My tenant was uninjured. We stood shivering in the dark for a short time until two couples in a car saw us and pulled over. They called 911 on their cellphone. Soon a tow truck, a police car and an ambulance arrived. We were taken to a hospital emergency room, where my arm was X-rayed; shortly after, we were released and went home.

The next day, I had several patients booked; I took one patient and cancelled the others, unsure of how I should proceed after injuring my arm and hand. I wanted to do my best to ensure that they would heal so I could continue my work. I remember that once I had gotten a terrible bruise on my thumb at a pool table, and my thumb had throbbed painfully all night. The next morning I found it dreadfully painful to treat my 10 a.m. patient, a little less painful for my 11 a.m. patient, and much better for the noon patient. By the evening, after I had treated patients all afternoon, the bruise was 70 per cent gone. From that experience, I learned that I should apply shiatsu to get my circulatory system to carry waste materials away from the injury and bring fresh blood to the area. That evening, the night after the accident, I had neck pain and a headache and I felt slightly nauseated. I did self-shiatsu to try to help the situation. For the next two days, I asked an associate to give me a treatment. She continued to do so whenever we could find the time over the next two weeks. Later, when the insurance company asked me how long I had to miss work because of the accident, I answered that I lost almost no time. In fact, the visible damage soon disappeared and my mobility was back in a week to 10 days, but the problem with my neck remained for almost three weeks. I continued to do self-shiatsu throughout that time, and I believe that without shiatsu, the damage would have taken three months or more to heal. It was a bad accident, and the car, a Lincoln, had $14,000 worth of damage done to it. I could easily have been killed; I knew how lucky I was to be alive. I felt a strong sense of mission after that – I believe I still have some work to complete in this world. One of the important things I feel I need to work on is the dissemination of shiatsu internationally.

One of the students I taught was a Mexican who came to Toronto to study, then returned to Mexico to offer shiatsu there along with other natural therapies at his clinic. He asked me to visit Mexico and give workshops, something I have done three times. I have always been impressed by the way the Mexican people I have met have welcomed shiatsu so warmly. My last workshop in Mexico was in February 1997. I flew to Mexico City and gave a lecture at its World Trade Centre; then I travelled to Orizaba in Veracruz, where an evening seminar was scheduled in the local hall and where I was interviewed by three radio stations. The seminar was organized by an accountant who had been terribly sick three years earlier with blood in his urine and genital bleeding. He had seen a succession of doctors but none could help him and he was ready to give up when he heard about my Mexican graduate's clinic. He felt skeptical but decided he had nothing to lose, so he went to the clinic for three weeks of shiatsu and other natural therapies. As a result of that, he recovered and became a firm believer in the benefits of shiatsu.

The man who owned the hall where the seminar was taking place had waived the usual $2,000 fee for us. The accountant's daughter told us that he was a millionaire. He was very depressed because his wife was dying of pancreatic cancer yet all his money could not change that fact or ease her suffering. He and the doctor had not told her that her illness was cancer. We went to his home that afternoon. I met him and his wife and explained shiatsu and natural healing to them, describing what they could expect from it and what they could not expect. The wife said she wanted to try shiatsu, so she and her sister and I went to the bedroom and I started the treatment. Half an hour later, my former student came in and asked in Spanish how she was feeling. She said that before I started she had felt pain all over, but the treatment relaxed her so that her pain was eased. I suggested she go to my graduate's clinic for regular shiatsu.

That evening, more than 300 people came to our seminar, including many local medical people. I introduced them to shiatsu, gave practical demonstrations, then answered questions. I was happy that evening. It was February 27; it would have been Toru's 66th birthday. Toru and I had worked hard together to spread the word about shiatsu throughout the world, and on his birthday here I was in Mexico addressing 300 people. I gave other seminars in Mexico, one in Morelos and the other in Acapulco, on the large property of the former director of tourism. Then I returned to Mexico City and flew back to Toronto.

I arrived home to some really good news. Denis Binks, a shiatsu practitioner in the Netherlands who had 20 years of experience, had been working hard to get shiatsu recognized as an official therapy by the European Economic Community. The preceding year, the parliament had recognized several therapies as complementary medicine, but shiatsu had not been included. I learned that on February 27 – Toru's birthday – the parliament had approved an amendment to the resolution so that shiatsu could be incorporated. Denis told me that 85 per cent of parliament had voted for this. It is clear that those of us who talk about our beliefs in shiatsu and its benefits for everyone are starting to see results. Whenever I travel, I hear more about how the time is coming for natural medicine and natural ways. I am delighted to see international movement in that direction. The body should not be a chemical dump any more than our outside environment should be.

In October 1999, the international shiatsu seminar was held in Buenos Aires,

Argentina, after a congress in Peru. While there, I heard the bad news from Matsuko Namikoshi that Tokujiro, who used to be very vigorous, had been growing weak since the spring of that year and was now in hospital. I was very concerned about his health and was anxious because I lived so far away. Tokujiro always told me that he would work as a shiatsu practitioner until he was 100 years old. In December of that year, I went to Tokyo to see him. I visited him every day to give him shiatsu treatments. I had handed out Shiatsu Academy Awards every year since the founding of the school. That year I did it in the hospital room. I awarded Tokujiro a medal, reading a note at his bedside: "Dear Mr. Tokujiro Namikoshi, You have created your original shiatsu treatment from your experience based on a hands-on therapy given to your mother. You have given us health and happiness, not only in Japan but all over the world. We admire your creation and promotion of shiatsu. We present you with the Shiatsu Academy Award, the Dragon and Hand medal. Dated December 1, 1999, Shiatsu Academy School Director, Kensen Saito." Tokujiro was pleased to receive this award. We toasted with ice wine, a gift I had brought him from Niagara-on-the-Lake, in Ontario's wine region. I had also brought a Marilyn Monroe calendar for him, and while he was staring at it, Kazuko Fujita, his secretary – who once gave shiatsu treatments to Princess Grace Kelly and her family in Monaco – said to him, "You should get married to a beautiful blond woman like Monroe next time around." Tokujiro responded, "No, I won't, because I can't speak English." I was relieved to hear his witty response. We burst out laughing. He was always very funny; in fact, for many years, he had been the chairman of a Japanese laughing club.

Tokujiro passed away in Tokyo on September 25, 2000, 10 months after my visit. He was 94 years old. People from all over the world took part in his funeral at Dentsuin in Koshikawa, Tokyo. Shiatsu never dies even though Tokujiro has passed on. All the students who were inspired by his passion to "promote shiatsu all over the world" continue in his footsteps. We reconvened in Madrid, Spain, two weeks after the funeral for the 13th international shiatsu congress, which had been planned for a long time, under the direction of Shigeru Onoda.

In the fall of 2001, the 14th international shiatsu congress took place in Rome, Italy. Dr. Fulvio Palombini, Rudy Palombini's son, presided over the opening ceremonies in a medical auditorium at the university. During the ceremonies, doctors from the Rome hospital connected to the university announced their support of shiatsu as an alternative treatment, and the audience acknowledged the announcement. Matsuko Namikoshi, who had taken over the Japan Shiatsu College from her late father-in-law, announced that the International Shiatsu Association (ISA) had been founded and had started promoting and educating people about the true shiatsu.

Eastern Europe welcomes shiatsu

On September 28, 2002, there was an international shiatsu seminar in Prague, Czech Republic. That was the first gathering in Eastern Europe. I heard through a Japanese embassy official that President Havel and First Lady Dagmar wanted to receive shiatsu treatments. An embassy secretary escorted Matsuko Namikoshi and me to the president's residence in a suburb of Prague that morning. Just two months before, the region had been deluged with heavy rains, causing the first serious flooding in a hundred years. The president's residence was so fine that I could not believe there had been disastrous flooding. Also, the rural landscape was very beautiful, especially in the early autumn. I learned that the president had been jailed on a political charge for 10 years, when the country was under Communist rule. He became the president after the revolution.

President Havel was operated on for lung cancer in 1996, but in recent years, he has been busy working for the causes of democracy and international cooperation and continues to do his best to look after his health. His wife used to be an actress (she is his second wife, the first having died due to illness). The first lady is beautiful and much younger than the president, so unfortunately she tends to be targeted by paparazzi. Soon after we arrived at their residence, President and Mrs. Havel, wearing dressing gowns, entered the drawing room. We went upstairs for the treatments. I treated the first lady, while Matsuko treated the president. The first lady asked me many

President Vaclav Havel and First Lady Dagmar Havlova of the Czech Republic (centre) pose with Matsuko Namikoshi and I after receiving their first shiatsu treatments, 2002.

questions through an interpreter. An hour later, she asked me, "Could you give us shiatsu treatments tomorrow and the day after tomorrow?" When I told her that I was leaving for Austria the next morning, she seemed disappointed. And so I promised her I would check my schedule to see if I could change my flight. After the treatment, we all went downstairs to meet the president, who had already finished his treatment, and the first lady went over to tidy his messy hair. After combing the president's hair with her hands, she asked the cameraman present if we could have our picture taken together while she was still wearing her robe. She was very friendly, warm-hearted and caring with everyone, especially her husband. When I was about to leave, she told me, "I am looking forward to your good answer this afternoon." On the way to my hotel, I decided I would find a way to see them again because they seemed to enjoy the treatment so much. I thought that Tokujiro and Toru would be pleased with my decision.

When I arrived at the conference, where shiatsu practitioners from the Czech Republic, Japan, Spain, Italy, Holland, Switzerland, America and Canada had all gathered, I received a congratulatory greeting from the Japanese councillor Keizo Takemi. Takemi is an internationally renowned political scholar who has profound knowledge of medical issues. His message said: "I am glad to welcome the international shiatsu seminar to Prague, Czech Republic. Last year when the international shiatsu congress took place in Rome, the International Shiatsu Association was founded and has since started promoting Japanese shiatsu all over the world. This is very positive. I hope that shiatsu will be acknowledged as preventive medicine and one of the treatments for rehabilitation. I encourage you to promote shiatsu to contribute to human health on an international scale. As people experience shiatsu's effects and have an opportunity to promote shiatsu, Japanese shiatsu will spread throughout the world. This is the first such seminar in Eastern Europe, and I hope that this will be a good chance to let people know about Japanese traditional shiatsu and will promote international goodwill. I pray for you in all your work and for the success of this seminar. Councillor Keizo Takemi."

For the following two days, I went to the Havels' residence with the interpreter and secretary. The Havels were able to release their stress and enjoy good rest, they no longer had any headaches and they felt healthier after only three days of treatments. The Japanese ambassador invited me to dinner in Prague that night. He told me, "I was touched by the news that the president himself experienced shiatsu, which was born in Japan; this has made history. I appreciate your enthusiasm, which will lead to a good relationship between Japan and the Czech Republic." I was grateful for his appreciation. Shiatsu had not only satisfied the clients who received it but had also inspired those around them to "live a happy life while giving happiness to others." That is the teaching of shiatsu-doh. When we achieve this, we are at last able to appreciate the joys in our lives.

After the Second World War, shiatsu was the only non-conventional medicine out of 300 researched to be approved by the Japanese government. It is somewhat frustrating to see that although it has been officially recognized by the Japanese health ministry, elsewhere we have to fight a major battle, country by country, for some sort of recognition. Researchers are learning more and more about the importance of hormones. They turn up new information all the time about the so-called "happy hormones" – such as serotonin, dopamine and melatonin. We have learned that people with Parkinson's disease, for example, lack dopamine. In fact, the body produces all these hormones as natural medicines. Our body is a veritable treasure trove of natural medicines. Why can we not mine our own body for these substances instead of taking them artificially? For me, shiatsu does not represent an alternative therapy. Shiatsu is always a natural form of healing. What exactly is medicine? Is it taking medications and cutting open the body? Should we consider this the conventional way and natural medicine the alternative? I personally believe it should be the other way around. The body is its own medicine chest, and the natural way is the best. More invasive methods should be considered an alternative only. Natural healing methods such as shiatsu often accomplish more than one expects. Patients often say that they initially came for shiatsu to deal with a particular problem, but after the problem cleared up they continued to come because they felt more energetic. They find that with shiatsu they can achieve more than they expected to in many areas of their lives.

Over a 60-year period, Tokujiro Namikoshi gave shiatsu treatments to many politicians, including 13 Japanese prime ministers. It is interesting that several of the politicians who went to him regularly eventually became prime minister. We shiatsu practitioners focus completely on our thumbs, fingers and palms when we are about to give shiatsu to clients, much like a sculptor who is about to chisel into a rock. In that sense, people who receive shiatsu treatments are a work of art.

Shiatsu helps everyone excel

Not everyone who has shiatsu regularly will become a champion or a prime minister. But everyone can tap into more of his or her own potential through shiatsu. Shiatsu liberates potential in the individual so that he or she is free to develop and grow. During shiatsu, there is a transmission from one person to another. It is something like going to the symphony. The conductor and the musicians make music, then the spirit of the music is conveyed to the audience as they listen, and it has an impact on them. Shiatsu works through the skin and sense receptors all over our body. When a needle touches our skin it is cold, whereas human touch has the warmth of the blood in it. Shiatsu is all about a comfortable, pleasurable pressure using the thumbs, fingers and palms, the most sensitive parts of the body. Artists transmit energy to an audience when they perform. Shiatsu is a healing art. It is not an intellectual process. Shiatsu's way is caring and communicating through touch. You have to have a treatment to appreciate this. Both patient and practitioner need to cooperate. The situation is similar to the hatching of an egg: when the time comes, the chick inside the shell pecks to crack open the shell; at the same time, the mother hen pecks at the same spot from the outside. Eventually, by pecking on the same spot from inside and out, neither too strongly nor too weakly, they break the shell and the new life is born. The cooperation between the patient and the practitioner during a shiatsu treatment is just like this. The patient wants to be healed and the practitioner wants to help with the healing. The patient feels pain at one spot and the practitioner presses that spot just the right amount, not too strongly or too weakly. In so doing, healing is born.

That is how the healing art of shiatsu works.

What I believe about the way of shiatsu is summed up in Tokujiro Namikoshi sensei's motto: "The heart of shiatsu is like a mother's love. Pressing the human body stimulates the fountains of life."

Tokujiro and I in front of the newly erected statue of him at the Japan Shiatsu College, dedicated on the occasion of his 88th birthday, 1992.

RESOURCES AND CONTACTS

Where can I learn shiatsu?
Shiatsu Academy of Tokyo
206–320 Danforth Avenue
Toronto, ON M4K 1N8
Tel: 416-466-8780
Fax: 416-466-8719
E-mail: sait131@aol.com
Website: www.kensensaito.com

The Shiatsu Academy of Tokyo offers a two-year, full-time, 2,200-hour Shiatsu Practitioner program, which begins each year in September. Classes are held Monday through Saturday. The Academy offers practical training and educates students in up-to-date shiatsu standards, theory, philosophy and history.

Where can I receive shiatsu treatments?
Professional Shiatsu Clinic
Shiatsu therapy is offered by shiatsupractors at two locations in Toronto.

Shiatsu Masters (Shiatsu Dohjoh)
Carrot Common Mall
206–320 Danforth Avenue (near
Chester subway station)
2nd Floor
Toronto, ON M4K 1N8
416-466-8780

Shiatsu Masters
Standard Life Centre
121 King Street West (at York Street)
Concourse Level
Toronto, ON M5H 3T9
416-366-8780

Student Clinic
The Shiatsu Academy offers student treatments in the student clinic at:

Shiatsu Academy of Tokyo
206–320 Danforth Avenue
Toronto, ON M4K 1N8
Tel: 416-466-8780

CONTACT INFORMATION

INTERNATIONAL ASSOCIATIONS

Japan Shiatsu College
2-15-6, Koishikawa, Bunkyo-ku, Tokyo, Japan 112-002
Tel: 81-3-3813-7354
Fax: 81-3-3816-3551
E-mail: www.shiatsu.ac.jp

PROFESSIONAL ASSOCIATIONS IN CANADA

National
Shiatsupractor's Association of Canada
101 Lonsdale Quay Market
123 Carrie Cates Court
North Vancouver, BC V7M 3K7
Tel: 604-986-4964
Fax: 604-986-4964
E-mail: info@shiatsupractor.org

Ontario
Shiatsu Diffusion Society
822 Broadview Avenue
Toronto, ON M4K 2P7
Tel: 416-406-5493

Shiatsu Therapy Association of Ontario
517 College Street, Suite 232
Toronto, ON M6G 4A2
Tel: 416-923-7826